Poppy

Happy Reading

All my love always.

Nan xx

HAPPY DOG DAYS AT THE PUG CAFE

HAPPY DOG DAYS

Anushka Fernando & Bertie the Pug

First published by Mirror Books in 2020

Mirror Books is part of Reach plc
10 Lower Thames Street
London EC3R 6EN
England

www.mirrorbooks.co.uk

ISBN 978-1-913406-41-7

Printed and bound in Great Britain by
CPI Group (UK) Ltd, Croydon, CRO 4YY

A CIP catalogue record for this book is available from the British Library.

1 3 5 7 9 10 8 6 4 2

Cover images: Depositphotos.com

For Fox & James, with love.

CHAPTER 1

Bertie

Go on, give them the gooey eyes.

I stared unblinking at the human, mustering up as much pug-eyed goo as possible. Which isn't the stare of a psycho-dog. No, I mean the goo of "puppy-dog eyes". Or, as Mamma called them, my "Disney" eyes.

I mean no harm! I'm a pug! You'll love me! Just like I love yoooooou!

The hand that held me, not with the gentlest touch I have to say, plopped me back down onto the newspaper next to Mamma and the last of my brothers and sisters.

"Well, he *is* the runt of the litter," Mamma's human said, almost apologetically.

I yapped, only to earn a tap on the nose from Mamma. There was that word "runt" again. Even if I didn't understand the exact meaning, I knew it didn't mean "Champion" or "Hero" or "Ace". All nice things Mamma said I was.

She also said I talked far too much, guzzled my milk too fast and was too playful, but you couldn't have everything. Although, excuse me, how could anyone be too playful? Besides, when you were the youngest you needed to get a woof in edgeways.

I heard the unmistakable snuffle of my eldest brother laughing at me. "Runty," he teased, so I cheekily nipped him on the tail, causing my sisters to pile in. Before you could say "Heel" we were climbing on top of each other, nipping legs, tails and ears. The humans noticed. One small one clapped her hands in delight and pushed her chubby finger through our wire fence.

"I want *that* one!" she said. And with that, my sister was whisked away for examination.

We fell quiet, exhaustion overcoming us, and snuggled in together, me cosy in the centre. Being in the middle was always my favourite spot. Hours later, I opened my eyes again when my sister returned smelling of strong perfume and sticky child hands.

"They'll be back for you next week, doll," Mamma said, licking her sadly. "But I'm so happy you have a home."

And just like that, one by one, my puplings disappeared. Until one day, it was just me and Mamma left.

"What am I doing wrong?" I wailed after yet another human plopped me back in our cage.

The smallest. The last. The feeblest.

"Feeblest?" I asked Mamma. These were more words I'd heard all too often. I tried to shrug off the names, but I'd begun to despair. "Why doesn't anybody want me?" I wailed to Mamma. By now, we'd been practising our gooey eyes together so often that Mamma told me I was the best of this litter.

"Those are liquid-brown eyes I could fall into, my son," she said. "I'm certain it won't be long until you choose your human." Me, choosing someone myself? That would be a fine thing. I'd be lucky to get any home of my own at this rate. "You're doing nothing wrong," soothed Mamma. "You're a special pug who'll make a special pet. You're just waiting for The One."

"But how will I know what The One looks like?" I persisted.

Mamma licked my ears as she thought for a moment. I guessed she was glad I was still here as she pondered her answer. "They'll smell thc best," she whispered. "But remember, when you've finally found them, what do you need to do?"

"Discover my Puggy Purpose, Mamma," I parroted. Just as she made us say every night before we went to sleep.

Discovering our Puggy Purpose is something every pug is taught as soon as we open our eyes. If we know what our purpose as a pet is, we'll have a doggy home forever. Mamma made us say this before we fell asleep every night so we'd remember long into our new life when we left her.

"Good boy," she grunted, nuzzling my ear. "Now, all you have to do is learn patience. And don't forget to feel pride. You may get stick along the way from bigger, faster dogs, or from humans who don't understand pugs, but always know that us pugs are unique. You're really very special."

*

After two more rejections, I began to lose what Mamma said I should never lose.

Hope.

She may have believed I was special, but would anyone else?

Then one afternoon, I was roused from my sleep for more visitors. On autopilot, I sleepily opened my eyes to switch on my gooey gaze. But this time, when I looked, an unexpected look was reflected back at me. This girl adult had big, brown eyes, rather like my own. And they locked onto mine as if… as if… she wanted *me* to fall for *her*…

She smelled different too. Not like artificial scent or sugary impatient baby hands. There was a fresh clean scent but also something else – and it took a while to put my paw on it. Then, aha…!

She smelled of sweet kindness.

This lovely human stood next to a man who looked equally happy. He even scratched the exact sweet spot on my ear. How did he know where it was?

"He's lovely, Anushka," he was saying.

She made a noise in agreement.

"I'm Anushka, and this is my boyfriend," she said to me softly. "A Man Called James." Anushka joined in by scratching my other ear. I closed my eyes briefly in appreciation. Her touch felt just like Mamma's. A Man Called James's touch wasn't half bad either. "He's *adorable*," Anushka said.

"He's the smallest one, and the last left," Mamma's human said. Fearing it would put them off, I concentrated my gaze on the man with as much goo as I could manage.

Don't put her off! I thought, as I glanced at Anushka, whose eyes were beginning to water. I could definitely see myself choosing her as my human.

She asked to pick me up and held me with such gentleness, I knew my nose hadn't failed me. She was kind and sensitive. I wanted to jump up and down, but managed to stay calm.

"James," she said. "Just *look at him.*"

"I'm lovely!" I wanted to bark, but held it in. The last potential owners hadn't appreciated barking. They feared it would worry their cat. Surely, that can only be a good thing, no? That's definitely one of my pug purposes. To bother as many cats as possible.

Just as I started to muse how lovely chasing a cat might be, I was lifted from the cage into something quite magical. A warm hug in the arms of this lovely human. You may not believe in love at first sight, but Puppy Love at First Sight does exist, I assure you.

*

After they left, I snuffled with delight as I ran rings around my tired mamma.

"I've found a human! The chosen one!" I sang, woofing in time to the thump of my excited heart. I ran around madly in what humans call a "zoomie", a crazy dash that means this was The Best Day Ever.

Mamma watched me, quietly smiling, until I exhausted myself and nestled down for a cuddle. Already, I smelled different. Of my new owners, their territory, my new future… but Mamma patiently licked my fur to calm me.

"See?" she said softly. "You just had to be patient. And once you're in your new home, you must remember what?"

"To discover my true Puggy Purpose, Mamma," I parroted.

The following day, we had one last snoozle together before it was time to say goodbye.

"Go well into your new life, my son," Mamma murmured into my ears. "You've struck gold with your lovely humans."

And with one last lick and a little whimper, I was boxed up and taken away from Mamma forever.

*

There was no time to cry though, as I was fascinated by all the jolting around in the box on wheels. Anushka and A Man Called James kept looking back at me anxiously as I peered from the back seat.

"Nearly home," Anushka soothed.

My new human's place was lovely and warm. Comfy sofa. Soft carpets. The Man Called James had shoes with a wonderfully chewy sole. They kept stroking my ears just the way I liked it and telling me what I'd repeated to my brothers and sisters for weeks.

"You're so handsome!"

When it came to bedtime, however, I didn't feel best pleased. I ignored the rubber bone and chewy ear they'd left for me and howled for the first few nights as they made me stay inside a tiny box called The Crate. I hated going in there, but eventually fell into a deep sleep.

Within a few weeks, things had calmed down and they started allowing me to sit with them while they stared at the light box. I couldn't wait to go outside in the cold air that I could smell from the window, but had to wait until the day

Anushka decided to carry me downstairs. She seemed very excited when she did.

"I've been looking forward to this, Bertie," she said. They said "Bertie" whenever I wandered into the room and seemed so delighted when I turned my head at the sound that I guessed this had become my name. "We can hopefully make lots of friends," she continued, "on our walkies."

I had no idea what this new word "walkies" meant until the fresh air hit my nose and what seemed like 1,000 scents overcame my senses.

Tomcats, foxes, mice, other human feet, breeds of mine I couldn't quite put my paw on, and then… pugs! I could smell lots of them. I was so excited at one small tree that I stopped for ages, snuffling into its base. Oh heaven! A female pug. Young, like me. She'd only been here to do a quick squirt, I'd say about half an hour earlier. She was healthy, energetic. Had eaten chicken for lunch. Probably a good laugh. Just missed her! Ah, next time.

Anushka tugged impatiently at her lead. "C'mon, Bertie, or we'll never get to The Park!"

We carried on. I tried not to stop too many more times, though I did pretend I needed a few phantom pees to get a closer sniff of certain areas.

"We can check your correspondence on the way back!" Anushka laughed.

And then we turned the corner… and ta-dah!

The green field known as The Park was wide and overwhelming. Straight away, I could see dogs on the other side, chasing around their owners. I strained at the lead with absolute glee.

"Hang on, Bertie, careful now!" Anushka was nervous, I could tell, so I stood quietly by her side. Protectively, I hoped, as she bent down. "It's okay, Bertie, my boy, thank you for waiting. I just…"

She swallowed hard as she glanced at the other owners, all whistling to their dogs or chatting to each other. They seemed to know one another, and for some reason this made Anushka's heart quicken. I could sense it.

She let me off the lead and I went for a little run. All of us pugs love doing a zoomie in a circle – they say we look like fat rabbits (rude!). They love to take out their screens to nab pictures and videos.

The great outdoors is bigger than you'd think, and it's why us dogs like to keep our humans tied closely to us. So I kept a close eye on Anushka. I wondered if she wanted to shelter from the drizzle that had started to wet the grass, or if she was just keeping away from the strangers. I wouldn't blame her for wanting to escape the rain. Us pugs loathe getting wet. Weirdly, the humans don't tend to mi[illegible] their sky tents and fixed expressions. It se[illegible] screwing up their faces and holding their hands to the sky. It bonds them together, giving them something to talk about. They can be strange sometimes.

I braved the wet and sniffed as many feet and hands as I was allowed, showing Anushka they were safe, before running back to her. "Come on!" I woofed. "Come and join in the fun!" I circled around her doing my fastest zoomie yet, yapping.

She looked down with amusement. "Go on, Bertie. Go and make new friends."

"But I want you to come…" I yelped. I ran back to the other humans and then back to my own. "Come on! Over here! I'll introduce you."

She giggled, as if I was playing a game. Which I loved, but right now, I wanted her to come with me. As the other dogs' humans chatted in a huddle, mine sat down on a bench alone. I ran around her one more time, my tongue lolling, a big smile on my face, hoping she'd get the message. But instead, she pulled out her pocket screen and sat staring at it. I barked and she smiled, gently batting me away.

"Aww, Bertie. I'm okay. Don't let me stop you."

"What's wrong with you?" I snuffled. "There are humans over there, all laughing together. Their dogs like me and they'd like you too, if only…"

And suddenly…

Boom.

Her anxiety made my nose tingle, but it was mingled with something else. Sadness. And what was that? Loneliness? I could smell the need, the want, but also, something else… the *fear*. I stopped dancing around and nuzzled her ankle.

"Oh, are you keeping me company now?" She laughed, rubbing my velvety ear.

"Yes!" I woofed. "Until you find friends of your own!"

But she stayed firmly put on the bench, scrolling with her fingers on the screen. Only at the end did she say how happy she was I'd enjoyed myself and promised me another visit soon.

On the way home, I was so excited thinking about our next trip to The Park that I hardly noticed the pain in my back. But by the time we arrived home, I found myself whimpering on the big, long, comfy seat where Anushka settled herself as it grew dark.

"You're very fidgety tonight, Bertie," she said. "Come and sit down." But it hurt, so I lay down next to her instead.

"He's exhausted after all that running around." A Man Called James smiled.

*

By the time the sun came up, I woke to a terrible smell.

"Oh no, have you had an accident, Bertie?" cried A Man Called James. He sounded more worried than cross.

I looked over my shoulder and barked my apologies. I knew better than this. He quickly cleared up the mess, but by the time he had finished it had happened again. Worst still, my back legs had gone from under me. Anushka yelled for James to grab the doggy box and a blanket. She was taking me somewhere I'd heard all about and hoped I'd never have to go.

The Vets.

The Vets was an assault on my senses, leaving me quiet for once. Scents of every single breed of dog I'd heard of, along with every cat and even birds and other species I'd not come across… I was overwhelmed by fear. By now, my back was hurting so badly that I could barely stand, so I focused on staying still as a lady in a white coat pawed at me. She spoke in hushed tones, but didn't seem overly concerned.

We went home, only for Anushka to stare at me with a very worried expression as I tried and failed to stand on the kitchen floor.

"Right, that's it," she said. "We need a vet's second opinion."

Within a few shakes of my tail, we were back at a different The Vets. I was on a high table that smelled of a very scared

Alsatian who had been there only a few minutes previously, I could tell.

Oh no, I thought. *If an Alsatian was this scared, what's going to happen to me?*

This time, a man in a white coat looked at me with a worried brow.

You know those moments in life when things are starting to go right but then they go horribly wrong, and you wonder why you dared to be so happy in the first place?

Isn't it what you humans call Dog Days? Well, this day was turning into one of those.

Anushka's warm hands were stroking my ears. As the vet's lips moved, her hands began to tremble. I turned to lick her better, but pain shot through my neck.

My human gently pressed my ears to my head as if she didn't want me to hear. The sound of her voice matched the tremble of her hands. "When do you want to do the operation?" she asked, in a wobbly voice.

Her eyes were watery, so I knew my cue. I lolled out my tongue to lick them away, just like I always do. But as I tried to stand, my damn legs splayed on the table and a hot rod of pain shot up my back.

"Dammit," I thought as I gave up, panting.

I was taken to a new The Vets, called Fitzpatrick Referrals, which I'd seen on TV. It's on a show called The

Supervet – I love to bark at the screen, especially when the dogs turn up. The main vet was called Noel, and his friend Colin was going to help me get better.

Soon, I found myself in a new cage with a blanket that smelled of their kindness and home – something I was already pining for. And they were leaving me.

"Now, this will all be over soon," Anushka assured me. "We'll be back in the morning."

She looked gutted to be leaving. But for me, it was far worse. Before we even open our eyes as a pup, we're warned of the dog kennels, the dog homes, the Sea of Batter and the place of no return… *Put Down.*

I shivered a little as I closed my eyes, trying to calm the memories of those warnings from my elder brothers, when I smelled a distinctive whiff of fish. My nose went wild as I strained towards the cage door. Yes. That was definitely a cat yawning. I wasn't alone after all.

"Hey, pug face," miaowed a voice in the dark. I could hear him but couldn't see the tom. He spoke with a strange transatlantic drawl. Some of the more pretentious kinds of moggy talk like this, my sister once told me. "Just woken up. Man, that was a deep sleep…" he said. "Oh no. No… No… No…"

"What? What's happened?" I woofed.

The tom was pacing his cage now – I could hear he was

agitated. "They've gone. Aww, maaan. They've lopped off my *balls*."

"Balls!" I woofed excitedly, trying not to jiggle my tail too hard because it hurt too much.

"Not those balls, dumb dog. My tomcat balls!"

"Ewww," I yelled softly. "Sorry to hear that."

"I thought I'd escape it, but I'd heard that's what they do. And to think they call owners 'responsible'. No more late-night wailing at ladies by the bins for me."

I couldn't help but laugh, though it hurt my back when I shook. "Happens to the best of us, fella. Mine will go no doubt soon too."

"What you in for?" the tom asked. "I'm Marmalade, by the way."

"Bertie, the pug. I have a sore back, but my human says they'll fix it tomorrow."

"Ah, thought I could smell pug. You pugs are like the royal cripples, aren't you? Too much inbreeding, man. You wanna mix up those genes, be a tom like me."

"Cheeky!" I tutted. I sank back down again, thinking I should have known better than to even try having a friendly conversation with a cat. Especially one above his station like this tom.

"He he, just a little joke," Marmalade said. "It's a dog's life, right?"

I ignored him and focused on licking my paw and breathing in the scent of Anushka from the soft blanket. Pesky cats.

He fell silent, both of us just listening to the round tick-tock on the wall.

"You sure your owner's coming back?" Marmalade said, slyly. "I mean, I heard you dogs need to know your purpose, otherwise they dump you. Sad, isn't it. Being so… *dependent.*" He hissed the word "dependent" as if it was a dirty word. Cats are like that. They wear their lack of need for human company as if it's something to be proud of.

Despite the pain, I found myself sitting again, my ears pricked up. What did he mean? I whimpered a little. He was pressing all my buttons. But then I thought of Anushka's kind face and our little trip to The Park and the way she looked at other dog owners.

"Yes!" I barked. "Yes… I know my purpose!"

"Oh really?" Marmalade continued. "Because you know what happens to dogs if they don't understand their owners, don't you?"

He made a strange noise, and I imagined him to be slowly drawing a claw across his throat.

"You're a tease," I barked. "But I do know! I do know my Puggy Purpose!"

Truth was, I'd been wracking my pug brains all week. *What do I need to do to help Anushka? Why have we chosen each other?*

The law of dog says, ideally, you should know within the first six months but also review it on a yearly basis. With Anushka, there was something I couldn't quite put my paw on.

I thought of her in The Park. Looking lost and lonely. I thought of her not speaking to the other dogs' mums and dads. And that sad anxious look and then… just like that… the truth hit me like a ball in the head.

Finally, my Puggy Power flashed like a neon light, as the knowledge of my purpose hit me square in my squashed face.

Anushka needed me… to help her make friends.

My human had become mine so I could introduce her to other humans. My tail started to jiggle-jaggle again, pain or no pain.

In The Park that day, it was loneliness I could sense. She was too shy to join me. But next time, I would take her with me. I knew how to make friends with other dogs, and all she had to do was come along for the ride.

It would be The Best Day Ever.

"My purpose is to help my human make new pals," I yelled through the cage. "We haven't had a chance to get started because of my back. But as soon as I'm fixed, I'm on the case!"

Marmalade fell silent again, probably disappointed by my confidence. Cats hate nothing more than a confident dog.

"Well… good for you," he miaowed back eventually. "You can sleep easy then, knowing they'll definitely pick you up."

Satisfied, I nestled down onto the blanket and found myself looking forward to tomorrow. Because the quicker I got better, the quicker I could help Anushka.

CHAPTER 2

Anushka

Anushka stared at the vet, a tall man called Colin, trying to absorb his words. Words that were too horrible for her to contemplate.

Her gorgeous new pug puppy, Bertie, adopted just eight weeks earlier, had collapsed on one of his first walks to the park. As if he was a puppet on a string, Bertie's legs had buckled beneath him, leaving him howling in pain. Anushka rushed him to one vet who suggested it was just a sprain, but her strong dog-owner instincts told her that it was something more serious. Insisting on having a second opinion had been the right thing to do.

Colin was now telling her that Bertie could die. He had the gentlest voice and the kindest manner, especially for a time like this. He warmly gave Bertie a pet name, calling him "Bertie Pumpkin", something Anushka was grateful for. Especially as his explanation sank in.

Bertie had hemivertebrae, an agonising condition in which the vertebrae (bones) in his spine hadn't formed properly. Her little dog, already the love of her life, faced a lifetime of pain or a very risky operation. Neither was good news.

"Bertie may never wake up," Colin warned. "Or he may be paralysed for the rest of his life."

Anushka pressed the soft ears of her pug close to his head to shield him. The vet's voice was a tone of doom. In any small way, she longed to stop her darling puppy suffering any more than he needed to.

Colin gently explained that this was a complicated operation and would involve making a 3D-model of his spine so surgeons could delicately work out how to piece him back together with metal rods. It was groundbreaking surgery – and necessary.

"He's a young dog, and this is his only chance," Colin said. "It's what I'd recommend."

"Okay," Anushka said, drawing breath. "Let's go for it."

Half an hour later, the forms were signed. Bertie was checked in to the Fitzpatrick Referrals practice, where Supervet Noel filmed his TV series. Colin was one of the vets who worked with him.

Bertie was in the best hands. When Anushka said goodbye, she gently held his velvet ears, ears she already knew like the back of her hands, and kissed the top of his head. Inhaling the scent of his fur, a sweet smell that reminded her of popcorn, always made her feel better. Everything about him was a tonic. He *had* to be okay.

"You'll soon be back to your old self," she soothed him. "I promise." She didn't know this, but saying it aloud helped. The way he looked at her did too – his brown eyes gazing up in trusting adoration. No, she couldn't let him down. If he needed a miracle, he was going to get one.

Colin watched them both and nodded. "We'll do our very best," he said.

Anushka bit her lip as she helped her boy into his wire cage. His face slipped into one of confusion as he was taken away into the back of the surgery to wait.

"Be strong!" she found herself calling after him before her voice cracked. It was time to be strong herself too.

Anushka brushed tears from her cheeks as she walked back to her car. Sitting in the driver's seat, she wound down the window to take some deep breaths as she gathered herself. Ever since she'd clapped eyes on Bertie, it had been love at first sight. He was the smallest and weakest of his litter – the pug left behind at the breeder's, waiting for his forever home and losing hope. But without a doubt, he was waiting for her.

They say a dog chooses their owner. A fanciful idea, Anushka had always thought, until Bertie had clearly chosen her. He'd stopped everything to sit to attention when they'd entered the spare room at the breeder's home. Then, he'd bounded over to her boyfriend James's outstretched hand over the cage fence and sniffed it enthusiastically.

Once Anushka had gently picked up this bundle, the pug immediately licked her face as if it was the most delicious treat. Like he could taste a sense of belonging.

"I'm Anushka," she'd said, by way of introduction. "And this is my boyfriend, a man called James."

She and James had caught each other's eyes, laughing at the formality. Somehow, all three had known this was a defining moment – something to remember forever. A moment to tell the grandchildren of when – and how – they first met their new dog. When the two of them became a trio. As if reading their minds, Bertie had jumped up between them so they closed into a circle together.

"Well this is it, isn't it?" James had said.

The choice was made on the spot. They were Bertie's new owners – and that was that.

Ever since she was a teenager, Anushka had dreamt of owning a pug. While some girls idolised boy bands, reality TV stars or Hollywood hunks, Anushka's pin-up was a pug. With keyrings, pug screensavers and posters, she didn't care when her older sister, Lakmini, teased her about being a crazy pug lady.

"That's a compliment." She'd laughed. Way into her early 20s and beyond, Anushka carried on hoping that one day she'd be in a position to give a pug a home.

But she had to wait many years before this happened. Renting flats in London where no pets were allowed meant a dog remained a pipe dream. Being in a position to afford to keep one was another factor. Working all day in an office also didn't help. It wasn't until she'd bought a small flat with her new boyfriend, James, and found a job near home that the impossible became possible.

They'd barely unpacked the last box after moving in before Anushka was calling reputable breeders to research dogs who needed a home. Meanwhile, as they settled in, they talked of their fantasy pug. They'd name him Harrison. They discussed the colour of his collar, whether they'd dress him up or just stick to harnesses. Whether they'd feed him dog food or cooked meals. They'd teased each other about where he'd sit when they snuggled on the sofa to watch a box set.

"On my lap, of course," Anushka said, imagining what Harrison would feel like. "Or between us?"

James laughed. "We may need a bigger sofa then."

They even had imaginary rows about where they'd let Harrison sleep at night. While Anushka insisted he should be allowed in their bed, James said it was unhygienic and the pug would definitely need his own dog bed.

The dilapidated kitchen in the new flat might have been beyond repair, but it became a job on a list for tomorrow. Buying a pug came first.

When finally that pug came home, the name Harrison didn't suit him, so the pug became Bertie. He wasn't just a much longed-for addition to the house – he'd turned their new house into a home. That's why it was unimaginable anything could happen to him now.

*

Anushka paced her living-room floor. Five long steps one way, eight shorter steps back. With Bertie's favourite soft toy, Donkey, clutched in her hands, she eyed her mobile phone on the sofa. It screamed an eerie silence.

"No news is good news," she muttered 1,000 times. "Come on, Bertie. I know you can do this."

She decided to break the worry-loop in her mind with a cup of coffee, so turned her stride towards the kitchen. As she filled the kettle, her mobile erupted into life. She ran back into the living room and frantically dived for her phone.

"Hello?" she said when she answered it.

"Bertie is out of the theatre and stabilising," Colin said. "You can collect him tomorrow."

Anushka's voice cracked as she said "thank you" several times in different ways. With relief. With gratitude. With love. Bertie had survived. He was coming home!

*

First thing the next morning, on the way to the vets in the car, another furry face appeared in Anushka's mind. Her old childhood dog, Frazzle.

Frazzle had been a beautiful rescue collie from Battersea Dogs Home. He was black with brown splodges, which made him look like her favourite Frazzle crisps. Her mum had brought him home one day, and he'd immediately become her best friend.

But unlike Bertie, he never survived an unexpected illness. Wincing at the memory, Anushka thought how special he, too, had been.

Frazzle had been there when Anushka felt particularly alone. Growing up with parents on the verge of divorce hadn't been easy. Both born in Sri Lanka, her mum and dad had been brought together through an arranged marriage but it was anything but happily ever after. Chalk and cheese went nowhere near to describe what different people they were.

Her mum was outgoing and fun-loving, always arranging gatherings with the local community, the driving force of the family. Her father, though, was more reserved, working long hours as an engineer. Opposites attract, but not perhaps if you're so mismatched in the first place that you have nothing to talk about.

Not speaking to one another became the norm for a couple who, in an ordinary life, probably wouldn't have chosen even to be friends. By the time Anushka was old enough to understand what love was, the only way her parents communicated was through hastily scribbled notes to one another. Whether her mum was leaving instructions on what to cook for dinner or where after-school activities were held, her parents chose not to speak to each other. For them, a pad and pencil made their marriage more tolerable.

But not for Anushka.

She grew up in a house as silent as a mausoleum. On the rare occasions she visited friends' houses, the difference to her own home was stark. Other parents laughed and joked with one another, or at least had polite conversations. Anushka quickly understood that her family set-up was unusual, so she stopped inviting friends over for tea.

Anushka's personality shrank into silence. She felt misunderstood by everyone. But, thankfully, there was always someone in the house who understood her.

Frazzle.

He knew when she was upset. When she was overtired. When she felt lonely. While her parents worked all hours, he was the one pleased to see her after school. The one who sat close by her, sharing the deep warmth of his body on the sofa watching children's TV. The one who said "Good morning" and "Good night" to her in her bed, with a lick and a lopsided doggy grin. He was the warm, furry constant in her life. Who listened without judgement. Who she couldn't be without.

Leaving the house to take Frazzle for a walk was the highlight of Anushka's day. With Frazzle ambling contentedly alongside her, she felt less self-conscious walking around the neighbourhood alone. With him by her side, her confidence grew, and she'd even smile or wave "Hello" if someone saw her.

One day, the day before she began secondary school, Anushka came home from a walk with Frazzle to find Lakmini looking upset. She followed her sister upstairs into her parents' bedroom to see her mother's side of the wardrobe empty. Lakmini quietly explained that their parents had decided to separate. Anushka fled to her room to cuddle Frazzle. He was the only being who could comfort her.

The next day, Lakmini got Anushka up for school and watched her like a hawk as she ate breakfast. This was the way things would be from now on, and Anushka settled into her new school as The Quiet One. The one who seemed to prefer the company of her dog to people.

Frazzle, her dear Frazzle, became even more of a rock to Anushka.

While her world turned upside down, he remained ready to put his chin on her knee or wag his tail with delight or press his warm, heavy body alongside hers on the sofa. Frazzle kept her safe and cosy, inside and out.

Anushka repaid his loyalty by taking care of him. She always made sure his food bowl was filled to the brim, and that he had fresh water and a long daily walk to the park and back. Come rain or shine, this was their routine.

*

One Thursday afternoon, when rain was coming down in stair rods, Anushka put Frazzle on his lead and walked to the park.

An hour later, they returned sopping wet. Anushka thought it would be funny to dry Frazzle with her hair-dryer. After all, it would save her sister from needing to wash another towel.

"Come on boy." Anushka smiled as she turned on the lowest setting so she wouldn't burn him. Frazzle panted with his tongue, looking as if he was smiling at her, his fur flying in different directions. He wagged his tail as she ran the hairdryer up and down his back, giggling at their newfound game. Imagining she was a dog groomer, Anushka pulled out her brush and gently stroked the top of his head.

"Feels nice, doesn't it?" She grinned. "You're going to have the shiniest coat in the park tomorrow."

Frazzle sank down onto his haunches as their game carried on. At first, Anushka thought he was dropping off to sleep, soothed by the warmth and her touch. It was only when he collapsed onto his side that she realised something was wrong.

A seizure gripped his furry body, making him shake from head to claw.

"Frazzle!" she screamed. "What's the matter?"

In a blind panic, she fled downstairs to ring her father from the phone in the hallway. He was at work in a shop, a new full-time job at which he spent what felt like every waking hour. Anushka explained what had happened, but her father couldn't just leave the busy shop. He promised he'd come as soon as possible.

By the time she ran upstairs, Frazzle was lying on the floor, perfectly still.

Anushka curled her arms around his head, pressing her cheek against his. He was still breathing. He was alive! But as they waited for her father, his body stiffened and shook violently again. And again. And again. Anushka's tears soaked his fur, while she watched with helpless horror as more seizures gripped her exhausted dog.

Finally, the key turned in the front door and her father appeared in the doorway, flushed with the effort of running.

"I'm taking him to the vets," he said, scooping up Frazzle in his arms.

Anushka had to wait at home. Her dad suggested it was best she didn't come. After all, he wanted to shield his youngest daughter from any more upset. She'd already dealt with enough lately.

For the next two hours, Anushka sat on her bedroom floor, stroking her hairbrush that was filled with Frazzle's brown and black fur, feeling more alone than ever. Whenever there's a gap in knowledge or understanding, children always fill it with their versions of events. In this story, Anushka decided what was to blame for the harm that came to Frazzle.

She was. And the hairdryer. It was her fault for turning it on.

Dogs died in hot cars, so it made sense to her child-like logic that the hot air from the hairdryer was somehow to blame.

Hours later, her dad returned empty-handed. Alone. The look on his face told Anushka that Frazzle wasn't ever coming back.

"I'm so sorry. Frazzle died," he gently explained. "He had a brain tumour, and there was nothing the vet could do to save him."

Anushka hugged the hairbrush to her chest and quietly sobbed. She was never able to articulate the pain she felt. After all, nobody understood her in the way Frazzle did.

At the time, she was also convinced that her father had made up the brain tumour story to make her feel better for killing her beloved dog.

From that day onwards, Anushka lived each day with a dog-shaped hole in her heart. Frazzle left an impossible gap to fill. Now he was gone, she had no one.

*

As her heart echoed with this childhood grief, Anushka nearly missed the turning for the vet's car park.

She pulled in her car and turned off the ignition to sit for a moment in remembrance of the first doggie love of her life. It had taken about five years for her to stop blaming herself for Frazzle's death, following many chats with her concerned father. He begged her not to blame herself, but she couldn't help it. Only as an adult did she fully understand her childish logic was flawed.

All she had left was one dog-eared photo of Frazzle – still

in a frame on the windowsill at home. She'd even kept the hairbrush with his fur for years, until it accidentally got lost in a flat move.

Until she'd brought Bertie home, she hadn't realised something had always been missing since her beloved dog died. Although she'd found love with James, it wasn't until Bertie came bouncing into their lives that she felt complete again. And now it was time to bring him back home.

Yes, this had been a bumpy start for Bertie, but now Anushka was even more determined to help him recover so he could lead a long, happy life. Bertie the pug had already brought so much joy into her world.

Somehow, this felt like a second chance for both of them.

*

Very slowly over the next few weeks, Bertie grew stronger. Thankfully, Anushka's boss in the office where she worked as a content writer even allowed her to bring him in, as he needed 24-hour care. Bertie loved all the attention from staff during the lunch hours, and, each day, the wag of his curly tail became faster.

Within a week, he was well enough to go outside for a sniff around and a night-time pee. Things were finally on the up!

One evening, about three weeks after his op, Bertie stopped in his tracks as he watched another dog walk past across the road. His tail stopped wagging and he stared in awe. He had a look in his eyes as if to say he was unsure but was excited too.

"It's okay, Bertie," Anushka soothed him, reaching down to stroke his ears. "It's only another dog."

He hadn't seen another animal since he'd fallen ill. Watching Bertie's little face was a trigger for Anushka. As his big liquid-brown eyes followed the other dog around with a sense of curiosity, a familiar knot formed in Anushka's stomach.

The look on Bertie's face brought back those long, lonely lunchtimes at school and then, later on, at university, where she sat by herself in the library or her halls of residence.

She used to wait in her room for the other students to go out before emerging. Once, she even overheard some-one say, "That's the room where the girl who doesn't say anything lives."

What made her situation even more bizarre was that once she did meet people, Anushka was a smiling, friendly person. Everyone assumed she must have lots of friends.

Anushka now spoke to work colleagues, and of course to James. But she had no acquaintances and didn't see much of her family either. She loved her mum, dad and sister, but they were all busy leading their own lives. They caught up at Christmases and birthdays and other occasional visits. Each time they did, she found herself retreating into her anxious shell.

Anushka resigned herself to being someone who watched life happening to them without really experiencing any of it.

Now, standing on this dimly lit street waiting for Bertie to do his business, it was as if Anushka was reading her pug's mind. He longed to run over to the dog across the road. Bump noses, smell bottoms, do all the usual doggie things they need to do to make friends.

Not having friends certainly went against a pug's nature, as it did Anushka's. She thought about her sister, who was cheerful and charismatic – people warmed to her. But occasionally, she saw glimmers of sadness or anxiety in her and Anushka wondered how she had been affected by their home life. Maybe they had more in common than she first thought.

Back inside, she shared her thoughts with James. "Bertie has missed out on being socialised as a puppy," she said. "It's a really important milestone for a dog. If we don't socialise him, soon he could become afraid of other dogs and animals."

"Really?" said James, doubtfully. "But he goes to work with you every day? Your colleagues love to make a fuss of him."

"Yes, but," Anushka replied, "he doesn't need socialising with human beings. Bertie needs to find doggie friends. Otherwise, he'll grow up nervous around his own species."

She didn't add "just like me", but she could have done so. The last thing Anushka wanted was for Bertie to have no friends and feel as much of a social pariah as she did.

CHAPTER 3

Bertie

Anushka was carefully cutting out a photo of my head and sticking it on a piece of paper. She was smiling, telling me how handsome I was, so I licked her hand in agreement. It's always best to thank someone if they compliment you. Makes them do it again.

"Love you." I snuffled, panting my appreciation.

Ever since the man in the white coat had taken that blessed bandage off my middle and my hair had grown back, I felt more like my puggy self rather than a lazy tomcat.

The prospect of going outside was exciting too. I couldn't wait for our first trip back to The Park to say hello to everyone and make new friends. Yet Anushka seemed to have other ideas. She stared at the squiggles they call "reading".

"Come and join me, Bertie, for a dog walk at Stoke Park on Saturday, November 12th," she read aloud.

I cocked my head, quizzically.

"You need some doggie friends, Bertie, so I'm organising a meeting with other pugs," she said. "Who knows, it could make things easier if there are other pugs around. You seem to recognise each other. And if I get stuck for conversation, at least I'll have something in common with the owners!"

I barked with approval as she clapped her hands.

"You really do understand what I'm saying, don't you, darling?" She grinned.

I couldn't understand every word, but whatever was happening, she looked excited. And having your human excited is one of The Best Feelings In The World. She nuzzled my face as I inhaled her love. We made The Best Team Ever.

"I love you," I told her with my eyes. "I love you so much!" I woofed loudly for good measure.

*

I trotted proudly alongside Anushka as she stuck the posters up on a tree and in a shop window. I still had what they kept calling a "limp", but I called it my jazzy walk. It was getting better every day too.

Once again, I sensed Anushka's nerves. She muttered quietly about never having done this before, as she stopped to tape a photo of my face onto a lamppost. She was worrying people would take it down or neighbours wouldn't approve. Thankfully, it was high enough that no dog could pee over it. I didn't fancy dog pee on my face.

"Oooh, I can't believe I'm actually doing this, Bertie," she confided in me. "Goodness knows how this is going to work out. I mean, I haven't made any lasting friendships for ages. Luckily, you don't mind about me being Norma No-mates, eh?"

I did a pug-tilt of my head, not fully understanding, but I knew whatever it was, she wanted my help. This was my Puggy Purpose, just like Mamma told me I'd need to find.

Right there, beaming down on that poster, was my face. How handsome I looked, how friendly. I wondered how many others could fall in love with me. Many, I hoped! As any dog knows, whatever breed you are, there are never enough people in the world who can love you.

For a moment, we stood outside a cafe in which Anushka had put up a poster, to admire the view.

"You're so photogenic." Anushka laughed. I snuffled my approval, imagining that one day there would be an even bigger picture of my face on a billboard.

But let's not get ahead of ourselves.

Things were going so well until the big day drew closer. I sensed Anushka's lingering doubts every evening after work. Then one evening, she ended a phone call with a knotted brow.

"A local newspaper reporter has called," she told A Man Called James. "They've seen the poster of Bertie and want to cover the Pug Meet Up as a news story. I never meant for this to happen. What if nobody turns up? I imagined it would be a small group, if that. I don't want my name to be splashed over the papers. I realise not much happens in our town, but does a meeting of pugs really warrant newspaper inches?"

My puggy heart ached as I watched her, so I licked her hand and sat at her feet, staring up at her, willing her to come to me for comfort. What I'd noticed was that she was honest and outgoing with A Man Called James, but the lively spark seemed to just disappear when we were out and about. This was what made her human life hard. Thankfully, she came to sit down for a stroke, and then A Man Called James came over to stroke my head too. I closed my eyes with contentment, but with my ears pricked up waiting for the next appropriate response, as needed.

"Ahh, darling, I'm sure people will turn up," said A Man Called James. "And look at Bertie's little face. You're doing this for him, remember?"

Anushka glanced down and pulled me up onto her lap. I nuzzled into her shoulder, whimpering softly in agreement with A Man Called James. She took a deep breath and sat me on a cushion next to her as if to look at me properly. I sat up as straight as possible – my Regal Pug Pose. Usually it makes humans laugh or captures their attention. Takes their mind off all their endless human problems, which spring up every single day. "It's A Human's Life, you know," us pugs say. So much seems to go wrong! But that's why they need us to guide them through it. If you live in the moment and see the sunny side, something good always happens. So why can't they see it?

"Cheer up," I woofed as she smiled back. "I love you. That's the best news, isn't it?"

"Yes, you're right," she agreed. "This is for you, Bertie. I shouldn't lose sight of that."

*

I decided to name the big day "Bertie's Amazing Dog Fest". I imagined lots of chasing rabbits and blue skies and hands chucking us endless treats, but what we woke up to was sky water falling in streams down our window.

Oh dear.

I jumped over and pressed my nose to the cold glass. As much as I longed to go to The Park, this was most off-putting. If you didn't already know this, let me explain clearly.

Pugs hate water.

We'd rather walk over hot coals (no idea what this is, but Mamma Dog told me about it) than stand in the sky water for even a few seconds. Apparently, it's something special about our breed because we were made for emperors, special rich people, in a place called China, so we never went outside like ordinary dogs. So yes, water is a doggie downer.

Just as I thought about whining, Anushka pulled out her lead. "Come on, Bertie, time to get ready," she said. "We can't let people down, rain or no rain."

I didn't want to let her down either, so I shook my doubt off again. Oh well, sky water or not, perhaps a rainbow would appear and all would be well. *Best to be puggy positive*, I thought.

Anushka didn't usually mind rain. She just put up her rain tent and set off, only grumbling if her hair got wet. But that day, like me, she wasn't that impressed after all. In fact, her face matched the grey clouds.

"Oh Bertie," she said as she shut the front door. "I guess we'll see who shows up for a walk in the mud, then, won't we?"

As Anushka put on her lead, I grunted at the sky water, telling it to stop.

My curly tail wagged in excitement as we made our way down to The Park. The drizzle had eased so it was just about bearable if I wrinkled my nose a little harder. I couldn't wait to see who'd turned up to Bertie Fest.

When we turned the corner, I could feel Anushka's hand tremble a little as she held her lead, so I looked up and gave her my widest smile. "Come on!" I barked. "Just one foot in front of the other and we're there!"

As we stepped into The Park's entrance, I spotted a huddle of rain tents held by humans above a busy circle of pugs, all excitedly sniffing and chasing one another. My puggy heart sang so loudly that I thought it would bounce from my chest. One, two, three, four, five, six, seven, eight… so many pugs. I lolled out my tongue with absolute pleasure.

This truly was The Best Day Ever.

"Hang on, Bertie," whispered Anushka, as I whined for her to undo her lead. I barely had a moment to warn her to stay close before bolting off to fill my lungs with these most glorious puggy smells.

"Hello, hello!" I barked, as I sensed the ages of the dogs, what they'd had for their last meal and the smells of their homes and owners. One or two even lived with a cat. Urgh!

"I'm Bertie!"

"I'm Daisy!"

"I'm Lilly!"

"I'm Sherlock!"

"I'm Henry!"

"Percy here!"

"I'm Bruce!"

So many names, and I was struggling to match smells with faces. Pugs love to rub our faces into each other's, something not all dogs like doing.

Bruce was about four years old, by far the biggest pug, and he'd brought his human, Hannah. Daisy was a bouncy three-year-old, much loved, and ate a luxury brand of food I didn't like, but each to their own. She was joined at the hip with her sister, Lilly. They had the sweetest of faces. Sherlock, bless him, had obviously been around this park a few times, judging by the smell of him.

Henry and Percy made a comical pair. Henry was thick-set and grumpy, while Percy was much smaller and bouncy. I could tell they would be fun. They warned us off going anywhere near their human, Vicky, as they were so protective of her.

We chased each other around doing zoomies, while our humans shook hands or pointed proudly.

"I don't even mind the rain now, as this is The Best Day Ever," Sherlock cried, bumping noses with me.

Such was my excitement that I'd almost forgotten my Puggy Purpose. So I paused to look for Anushka. I had visions of her sitting on a bench somewhere alone, feeling sad or, maybe, even worse, she'd wandered off somewhere. But glancing at all the feet, I soon recognised her trainers before

I heard her voice. Looking up, I could see her chatting and smiling to Sherlock's owner, Kandeece.

"Thank you for arranging this meetup," Kandeece said. "It's a great idea."

"Oh, glad you're enjoying it," Anushka replied.

For now, Anushka was smiling so I ran off to play. The grass was damp, the sky was grey, but everyone's faces said it was sunny. And best of all, my human's smile matched everyone else's.

All too soon, it was time to go. I'd even left Anushka to chat to others as I played chase and catch up. As we said goodbye, touching noses, inhaling each other's scents for one last time, we promised to see each other again.

And so that was the story of how we all became friends. Except this involves human beings, so it's never as simple as that, is it?

*

When we got home, A Man Called James wanted to know all about it. I expected Anushka's face to be as happy as mine, but when she spoke her smile unexpectedly vanished.

"Oh yes, everyone seemed to like it," she said. "I mean, I *think* they did. The pugs certainly did – Bertie spent the entire time chasing them around. I guess I could have spoken more about myself. But I stuck to speaking about Bertie. Oh God, I hope people didn't think it was boring." Her tone was riddled with doubt.

Doubt is where most humans go wrong in life. Pugs don't doubt anything. We either love or loathe. We want or we don't want. Makes things super-simple when you think about it. If you live in the moment, there's no time to doubt. Okay, maybe I'd "doubt" if I was asked to jump up onto a table I couldn't reach or a big dog glared at me.

But really, doubting is *not* for pugs.

I wrinkled my nose with confusion. I didn't recognise her description of Bertie Fest at all! Every pug I smelled had the most incredible time of their entire lives. I was sure they'd spread the word at every lamppost. I couldn't wait until we all met up again. And we would all meet again, wouldn't we?

I licked Anushka's hand and she lifted me up onto the sofa. I had to tell her. She needed to know it was great.

"What's with the doubt?" I snorted.

"Well." A Man Called James laughed. "Bertie looks pretty happy about it, doesn't he?"

"Ha, yes, he does," Anushka agreed, tickling my head. "And he's why I arranged it in the first place. Ah, if only I could get along with people as easily as pugs get along with other pugs."

A Man Called James put his arms around Anushka, which

slowed down her breathing. That made me feel all warm inside, so I asked to join in.

"I'm sure they all liked you, Anushka," he said. "You're a lovely person who deserves to have more confidence and friends. Maybe focus on the positives. You got through it. Bertie is happy, and that was your goal, right?"

*

I woke the next morning desperately needing a pee, so I had to stand at their door and tell them. A Man Called James emerged, with ruffled hair like someone had given him a good stroke. He looked grumpy as he picked me up to take me outside.

"You've still got your John Wayne wobble going on, haven't you, poor boy?" he said. I didn't get what he was on about (not an unusual thing when it comes to A Man Called James, as often he finds himself funny when no one else does).

As far as I was aware, there was nothing wrong with the way I moved – the cheek of it. The pain wasn't so bad, but if he wanted to carry me around, who was I to complain? A carry always means a cheeky cuddle. Sometimes, he even zipped me into his coat. Us pugs get cold quickly, don't you know.

Back inside, Anushka was out of bed and making that horribly smelly drink they call coffee when her phone pinged. "Several people have now asked when the next Pug Meet Up is," she said, reading whatever was on her screen. "I really hadn't thought that far ahead. I mean, some of the owners were lovely, but I thought maybe we'd just say hi in the park on occasion."

*

Later that evening, I'd just eaten my dinner and was lying on my bed licking my paw, when A Man Called James walked in holding a newspaper. I stood to attention with my ears pricked up. I hadn't seen a real-life newspaper in this flat before, aside from peeing paper laid down in case of accidents. This was a freshly folded, brand new newspaper. Nobody had chewed it or even lost any pages. Drool began forming in the corners of my mouth as I imagined that delicious first sink of my jaws into the rolled-up paper.

"Mmmmmmhhh mhhhhhhh."

But A Man Called James kept it well out of reach, and Anushka's eyes widened when he showed it to her. They both looked like cats caught in a dog's glare.

"Look at this," A Man Called James said, pointing his finger at the words. "Guildford Pug Meet Up: playtime for pooches, at first-ever pug fun day in Stoke Park."

"Oh wow, it's a whole page written about our meet up," Anushka said in amazement. "I never imagined it would generate this much interest!"

I barked, doing my dance at their feet. I was interested in getting my teeth into that paper. Such a waste if they were only going to stare at it. Humans really don't know what they're missing.

A Man Called James pulled out the great shiny Silver Book – they call it a laptop, and I've noticed it occupies many hours of their staring time. It turns into a window that they love to watch or dance on with their fingers. I'm intrigued by the Silver Book, but, strangely, whenever I try to sniff it they panic and say things like "Whoah whoah, Bertie, don't knock it off" or "Eeek, careful, let me move that for you". Nope, they never let me have more than a brief sniff.

How can something you love so much make you so anxious? They should swap a laptop for me – their lapdog!

The Silver Book lit up into life, and both of them cuddled up together to gaze at it.

"Why don't we set up a Facebook page?" A Man Called James suggested. "For Bertie Fernando Morgan, the pug, and mention any Pug Meet Ups on there. That way, it takes the pressure off you, and people can even arrange their own meet ups if they like?"

"Good idea," Anushka agreed.

I did a little happy dance as she smiled. This was The Best Day Ever after all.

CHAPTER 4

Anushka

Anushka was so surprised by the response that it took several days to sink in. Far more people and dogs had shown up than she'd expected, and the local paper coverage had publicised it even further. Plus, the number of messages to Bertie's new Facebook page the next day had been mind-boggling.

There was a real gap in the market for pug owners in Guildford. Who'd have thought it?

On the one hand, it was heartening to see so many people keen to socialise with their pugs. But equally, the event's popularity, to someone like Anushka, was quite terrifying. She'd envisaged four or five pug friends for Bertie to chase round with a ball, and maybe a flask or two of tea being shared if the owners were so inclined. Instead, Anushka had become the organiser, was sought out for conversation and had to make *others* feel at ease. Not a situation she'd ever imagined finding herself in.

Thankfully, the chat had been focused mainly on their shared love of dogs, pugs in particular. Like all the owners, Anushka found herself fascinated by their stories and the varying puggy personalities. Conversations, much to her surprise, had flowed effortlessly – even if, afterwards, she felt rather exhausted, as she did after most social occasions.

But something was happening. More and more people were joining the special pug group. They swapped photos, admired each other's pugs and even offered to dog-sit.

One day, while skimming through messages on her laptop, Anushka let out a small sigh. A signal that Bertie instantly picked up on.

"Oh, Bertie," Anushka said. "This is lovely. But, and I know this sounds silly, this group is getting too big for me."

Bertie cocked his head and held it still, the way he did when offering a velvet ear to stroke. Anushka reached for it. Her dog was right as usual – this action made her feel better within seconds.

"You can't get me out of this pickle, though, can you, Bertie?" She laughed. "People want another meet up soon. What shall I do?"

Anushka had never sat down and analysed herself, any

more than most busy 20-somethings do. Social anxiety wasn't something she was conscious of. Feeling a sense of dread, especially when she was out of the comfort zone of her house, was simply a feeling she'd experienced since childhood. It was part of the fabric of her life, just as having a strong work ethic or loving pugs was. So naturally, she didn't believe it was about to change any time soon.

The longer she hid away, the harder it became to make friends, and the more people avoided her. The more she stayed in, the more she feared going out.

Sitting there next to Bertie, counting the pangs of her anxiety, she remembered the Christmas of her first year at university. She'd felt trapped in a cycle of fleeing home as soon as each term finished. She'd pretended to her sister and parents that she was having great fun, when really she'd been dreading her return.

Despite this, she graduated with honours. And sometimes, she felt that her shy nature made her more hard-working. She quickly found a job in fashion promotion, winging it during the interview, but after a few weeks, exhausted by the social aspect, she quit.

And so began a long cycle of jobs that would ultimately force her out of her shell. With all the will to break free, she kept locking herself back inside her shell, and her world remained small.

On graduation, she quickly won a freelance role on the beauty desk of a national magazine. Despite fighting off stiff competition, though, she never fitted in. This was a fast-paced glamorous world, and as soon as work finished she rushed home to her rented room, only stopping off at the supermarket to buy a meal for one.

Weekends were spent indoors, only to venture out to a cafe for coffee. Monday mornings were to be dreaded. Because the real world was always something Anushka observed from the outside rather than living in it. With her job in London and Lakmini busy with work and a serious boyfriend, the sisters who once were thick as thieves growing up, found they didn't see much of each other now.

"Fine, thank you," was her mantra.

It's what she said to everyone until people stopped asking. Because if someone keeps saying they're fine, it's generally accepted that it must be true.

The reality was, as years passed, Anushka viewed herself as the awkward black sheep of the family. Her mother was well respected, running a successful nursery business that she started with just a £2,000 overdraft. Her father poured himself into his work and found contentment in his involvement in a Buddhist temple, while her sister found a job for a designer label and married her long-term boyfriend.

The family reunited a few times a year. Little enough time for Anushka to fix her smile and pretend the deep pool of loneliness inside her didn't exist. When Lakmini had her children, daughters Ruby and Delilah, Anushka felt released from the strain of meeting up with her family, as everything could focus on the new grandchildren, whom she adored. They were the light of their lives and it really did feel like the family was coming together.

Besides, Anushka doubted anyone could do anything about her lack of social life or inner turmoil. It was embarrassing, wasn't it? Admitting you had no friends, no life outside of work. Keen to avoid seeming desperate, she always pretended she was busy. Desperate people are even less attractive to be around, she decided.

A documentary film at the time summed up all her worst fears. "Dreams of a Life" was the true and tragic story of a woman called Joyce who died at the age of 38 alone in a flat in London. Her body wasn't found for over two years as she didn't have any friends and was estranged from her family.

The idea that someone could become so removed from society frightened Anushka, because part of her could see herself succumbing to exactly the same fate. Despite longing to be part of things, she wasn't as close to her family as she wanted to be. If the worst happened, would anyone actually find out? Would anyone from work check if she was okay? She shuddered to think.

As far as Anushka was concerned, she faced a lifetime of being alone. Possibly eaten by cats at the end of it. Well, maybe not cats, as she still clung onto the dream of owning a dog one day.

Specifically, a pug.

Perhaps it was their naturally curious and sociable nature that attracted Anushka to them. A pug has no self-consciousness. In fact, they *want* people to be conscious of them.

When Anushka first spotted a pug in her hometown of Guildford, in the late 1990s, she couldn't believe what a sassy stride such a little dog had. It was as if a celebrity had livened up the high street. She even plucked up the courage to ask the owner if she could give his dog a stroke, and she immediately fell in love. Pugs oozed confidence with their cuteness. With their squished faces and saucer-like eyes you could get lost in, each had a character in their own right. From then on, she collected pug paraphernalia, the tackier the better, as the sight of a pug face never failed to lift her spirits.

The idea of owning a pug one day gave Anushka a goal – a future dream to hold on to.

*

Just as Anushka was embracing being a single crazy pug lady, James walked into her life by accident.

Her work colleagues had persuaded her to come out for a quick drink for someone's leaving do. Unlike London, her office in Guildford was far more easy-going and Anushka felt welcomed in by her warm and friendly colleagues so she happily went along. Unable to think of an excuse fast enough, this time she reluctantly went.

At first, when James approached Anushka at the bar, it didn't register with her that this handsome, funny man was actually flirting with her. By the time she realised this, she was so tongue-tied that she didn't know where to look. When he asked to buy her a drink, she agreed. She watched as he also ordered beer for his work colleagues and then a milkshake for himself.

"A milkshake?" she said, trying to hide a giggle behind her hand.

"What's wrong with that?" He shrugged, smiling. "I like milkshakes."

At that moment, Anushka realised that James was a man who walked to the beat of his own drum. He didn't care what anyone thought, and she found this oddly very attractive. They spent an hour chatting amiably, before James was pulled away by colleagues.

"I'll ring you," he promised. Anushka couldn't quite believe he would, but he did.

For their second date, James asked her to join him for a walk with his parents' dog. Sophie was an old spoodle, a cross between a spaniel and a poodle, who struggled with arthritic hips and walked with a limp. This may not have been the most romantic date idea to some people, but to Anushka it was perfect.

They talked non-stop. This was most unusual for Anushka, but James kept asking her questions…

What were her passions in life? "Easy – animals, especially dogs, and, oh, writing."

If she liked her job. "Oh, it's okay, some days are more interesting than others."

Where would she like to live? "I love the countryside of the Surrey Hills, so I'm happy with Guildford."

He listened so intently, as if she was the most interesting person he'd ever met. She'd never felt like this before.

James also didn't tease her when he spotted her pug key ring and the pug screen saver on her phone. He simply asked her what she'd called her pug when she got one. Feeling she could be herself with him, Anushka decided to confide about her aversion to socialising.

"It's amazing you actually met me in a bar because, er, I much prefer being at home," she said. "I don't have what you'd call many friends."

She half-expected him to put Sophie back on her lead and

make a mad dash for it. *Sorry Anushka, I didn't realise you're such a friendless saddo,* she thought he'd say. *I'm going now. Nice knowing you.* Her busy brain was always two steps ahead, imagining the worst. Worrying, always worrying...

Instead, James moved Sophie's lead to his other hand and gently slid his hand into hers. She was surprised by how warm and lovely his palm felt.

"I like you, Anushka," he said quietly. "You're the person I've been looking for. Can I please see you again?"

Nobody had ever said this to her before, but now they had done so it felt like the most natural thing in the world to agree to. When James took her hand, it seemed to fit perfectly into his.

Their relationship blossomed with an intensity that surprised them both. Over the next few months, Anushka realised that having someone love her made her love herself a tiny bit more.

A year later, they bought a small flat together in Guildford, and the next part of her dream came true. The fantasy pug became a reality. And, just like that, Anushka felt she had a future again. She'd found true love with a boyfriend and a dog.

The only continuous stubborn cloud was the fear of going out. In fact, she became reliant on either Bertie or James to go everywhere with her. From the outside, people always told her she appeared confident, bubbly even, but inside it was the same old story.

*

With the first Christmas in their flat fast approaching, Anushka was determined it would be a special one. Perhaps with James and Bertie supporting her, it was time to take the plunge and invite her family over.

By now, her parents had become good friends, bonding over their love of their granddaughters. They loved to make a fuss of the little girls, and spoiling them rotten was no bad thing. But Anushka couldn't help but fall back into her feeling of being the black sheep, fretting over any possible tensions at each family meeting.

Shaking the doubts from her mind, she started writing texts to tout the idea of inviting her family over. She now had her own flat, and life had moved on for her. She wanted them to be proud – to prove to herself and to them that she'd changed, that she'd grown up. Her parents loved animals, especially dogs, so were bound to fall in love with Bertie too.

She glanced at the calendar. Christmas was only six weeks away, and meeting her family wasn't the only thing on her mind.

"Maybe a Christmas theme," she thought, "is the answer for another Pug Meet Up. A Christmas fancy-dress competition in the park. If there's one thing pug owners love, it's dressing up their dogs."

The last thing she wanted was for everyone to be standing there shivering in the rain, waiting for something to "happen". Perhaps an event such as a fancy dress party would get tails wagging.

When James got home from work, Anushka ran the idea past him.

He laughed aloud. "I love it," he said. "I'll knock up a little poster, and you can write the invitation as if it's from Bertie."

James rolled up his sleeves in a theatrical manner, cracked his knuckles and began pulling up photos of pugs and Photoshopping Santa hats onto them. He smiled to himself, enjoying this task. This was a far cry from his usual job working for a financial company.

"Oooh, I didn't know you could use Photoshop," Anushka said.

He winked. "Jack of all trades."

Hours later, he had something on his laptop to show her.

"Voila," he said, with a flourish. Anushka peered at the screen to see a very amusing photo of Bertie. He was wearing a lopsided Christmas hat and standing with a few pug friends looking equally festive.

"All it needs is for you to write a good advert beneath it now." James grinned. "And those Photoshopped friends of his could become real ones!"

Taking a deep breath, Anushka sat down at her keyboard. At first, she kept writing sentences and then deleting each one. Nothing sounded quite "right". She didn't want it to sound as though *she* was writing the piece. She needed some inspiration. Looking around the living room, Bertie caught her eye, just as he was always on the look out for hers.

"What would I say, Mamma?" Anushka said in her Bertie tone of voice. She started typing yet again.

Come to my special pug Guildford Christmas Meet Up. 11am Sunday, 11 December. Pugs, Chugs, Pugaliers, Puggles and more welcome! Join us for sniffing, tail wagging, playing and lots of festive merriment. Prizes for best-dressed pug.

As Anushka read back her words with Bertie's voice in her head, she thought that if Bertie could use his paws, this is what he'd want to say. Pugs, especially, found small things not only something to appreciate but also mega exciting. And watching them, it was impossible not to feel the same way. Bertie wouldn't waste a split second worrying if any of the other pugs liked him. Or how many pugs turned up. All he needed was one friend to chase around and do a zoomie with.

"That's better," she said to herself. "Thanks, Bertie."

Before she posted the advert, Anushka hesitated for a moment. "I guess everyone needs cheering up during the long, dark December afternoons, don't they?" she said to James for some reassurance. "Any event is better than nothing on a grey December Sunday, right?"

"Of course," he enthused. "We'd go, wouldn't we? For Bertie. If someone else had arranged it. Well, they haven't, so let's do it."

Hearing his name and sensing a pensive mood, Bertie snuffled right at the correct moment as her finger hovered over the Send button. He looked at her with gooey eyes and did a pug tilt, as if to say, "Go for it."

As his owner, Anushka told herself, *I am simply doing it on his behalf.* This idea felt like a revelation, so without a second's extra thought, she pressed Send.

*

For at least an hour, Anushka felt giddy with her newfound confidence about the meeting. But, in bed that night, when Bertie woke at 4am, which he often did licking his paws loudly, it didn't take long for the inner critical voice inside her head to pipe up.

Who do you think you are, Anushka? Arranging a big local social event when you can barely look anyone in the eye! Are you crazy?

On the face of it, yes, she'd lost her mind, but it was too late now.

The invitation already had over 30 likes on Facebook. Pug owners were already excitedly discussing costume options. Would they get one from Etsy or make their own? Some pugs loved wearing hats, while others loathed it. The build-up was already full-steam ahead.

I'll just have to make the best of it, Anushka thought, as she tried to hush Bertie who was looking at her with a quizzical stare, his face lit up by the moonlight flooding in through the window.

"If you're awake, why can't I be?" he seemed to say, so she rolled over to pretend to be asleep, hoping it would encourage him to do the same.

The following day, after work, Anushka popped to the shop to buy a pug soft toy as a prize for a "Best-Dressed Dog" competition.

The day after that, a direct message landed on Bertie's Facebook page. It was from a photographer from the local newspaper in Guildford. Anushka gulped as she read his request to come and photograph the Christmas event.

Our readers love dogs, he wrote. *The last video went down a treat. So with your permission, we'd like to photograph the event.*

The word "event" sent a little shiver down her spine. It all sounded so… official.

What if it rained again? What if no one turned up? Anushka had visions of Bertie standing miserably in a sopping Christmas jumper in a muddy wet park. Of her apologising to people who'd turned up expecting some sort of Winter Wonderland dog event, when all they'd found was her and Bertie.

Once again, she confronted her instincts to run away and hide.

"Come on, this is for Bertie," she said aloud to gee herself on. Bertie's ears pricked up on hearing his name as she quickly typed a response.

Yes, of course you're welcome. The more the merrier, she typed to the photographer, channelling her inner pug.

Getting into the spirit that evening, she Googled pug costumes. There was every kind imaginable, from reindeers to elves to fairies. The dressing-up market for pugs was mind-boggling. Companies making dog harnesses, collars, bandanas and outfits were springing up all over the place.

As easy as it was to laugh at spoilt dogs, Anushka couldn't help thinking how wonderful it was too. When she saw how much joy Bertie had brought into their lives already, she too wished to spoil him rotten. And why not? The look on his face every time she bought him a new outfit or toy made her believe he appreciated it.

*

The big day of the meet up finally arrived. Anushka woke once again to see spits of rain hitting the window falling from grey foreboding skies, but she shook off her own sense of apprehension.

Bertie was already standing to attention between her and James, gazing at them with such an intensity that she was sure he understood which day it was.

"Come on, Mamma, get up," Anushka growled in Bertie's voice. "Time to put your glad rags on."

After breakfast, she pulled out a small red-and-blue Christmas dog jumper with a snowman motif that she'd picked up from a charity shop.

"Today is definitely the day to try this on," she said to Bertie, who looked less enthusiastic. But as she pulled it over his head and clapped with delight, he picked up on her mood and danced from paw to paw.

Then, it was her turn to pull on her own Christmas jumper, featuring a gaudy reindeer embroidered onto bright holly green. It was the first time she'd ever bought one. But it only seemed fair that if she was making Bertie wear one she did so herself.

Unbeknown to Anushka, James had bought himself a matching jumper. When he emerged from the bedroom wearing a larger version of her own, she didn't know whether to laugh or cry at first.

"Oh James, well, I guess all dignity has gone out of the window today then," she giggled.

Just before they left the house, Anushka swallowed down a last-minute bout of nerves. Part of her wished she could hide behind a huge scarf, but she told herself that today didn't have to be a big deal.

"It's just a small group of pug fans like us letting their dogs off the lead in fun costumes in a park. What could possibly go wrong?"

CHAPTER 5

Bertie

Oh man, I was so full but proud to say I kept going. Crunchy, moreish, mouthful after mouthful. The deeper I moved myself inside the bag, the more mouthfuls of delicious meaty heaven I found.

My jaws almost ached as I gobbled pieces of what they called Gravy Bones in this never-ending bag… Mmmmh, my curly tail couldn't stop jiggling as I opened wide again for another drool-inducing heavenly chomp…

"Bertie! Time to wake up. Oh, are you dreaming, my little boy? You're dribbling in your sleep."

Anushka was leaning over me, rubbing my belly. Ah, I'd been having The Best Dream Ever of The Best Day Ever. We'd been visiting A Man Called James's parents' house and I'd found a 1kg bag of Gravy Bones in the cupboard. By the time they found me, I'd eaten half the bag. A whole divine 10 minutes of chew, and even months later, I dreamt The Best Dream Ever.

Now Anushka was standing in front of me holding a small colourful jumper, I sensed a new Best Day Ever was coming right up. So I stood to attention and let her pull the jumper over my ears. Honestly? Cheesy Christmas jumpers weren't my style, but the way Anushka's face lit up like a Christmas tree when I wore what she wanted was irresistible.

She smiled at me. "It's our Christmas Pug Meet Up this afternoon, Bertie."

I lolled my tongue and waited for her to help me off the bed. I still couldn't jump down. Besides, this way, I always got to have a mini snuggle to tell her I loved her on the way down.

"Grrreat!" I woofed.

I made sure Anushka was firmly on her lead before we set off. A Man Called James came too. But as we walked off, it didn't matter how many times I lolled my tongue out on the way as Anushka's lips remained in a firm line, so I knew something was up. She kept her head down, clutching a bag with a soft toy I'd had my eye on all week. I hadn't been allowed to touch it, just like the Silver Book. That meant it was something special.

On the way, I stopped to sniff every few steps as usual, but I felt Anushka tug on her lead impatiently.

"Eh?" I snorted. "Where's the rush?"

"Bertie, we have to get to The Park. We don't want to be late," she said.

I sensed her anxiety. Oh no. Guess we'd better get to The Park then.

We turned the corner on Nightingale Road and walked across to The Park's entrance. Quickly, I spied lots of brightly coloured pugs dashing around the green. It was another Bertie Fest! Why didn't anyone tell me?

"Hey, I am hereeeeee!" I barked, waiting for Anushka to let herself go free before I dashed off into the crowd.

"Daisy! Sherlock! Doug! Lilly! Pearl! Henry! Percy!" All my new buddies were there. We all spun around and around, delighted once again to be together. We laughed at each other's dressing-up costumes too. Daisy and Lilly were sparkling fairies, Pearl was Mother Christmas, Henry and Percy were elves, and Sherlock was a Christmas pudding.

"I look bloody ridiculous," snuffled Sherlock.

Doug smiled. "But look how happy our humans are!" He was wearing a simple holly leaf collar.

Daisy gave her ladylike woof as she spun around with her festive harness, matching with Lilly, who ran around like the loon she is.

In my excitement, I forgot to check on Anushka. She was looking in her bag for something, but I could tell she was just pretending. There was never anything in that bag apart from receipts and fluff. While A Man Called James walked around, shaking people's hands, pointing at pugs, Anushka kept herself busy.

I realised Anushka needed introducing, so I made a mad dash over to one of the humans, Daisy's human, called Kelly W. I sat on her foot so she stopped talking to Sherlock's owner and looked down at me.

"Hello you," she laughed. "Is it comfy down there on my Wellington boot?"

Just as I'd planned, Anushka noticed and rushed over to say sorry to Daisy's human.

Bingo! I sat back panting as they started chatting.

"Sorry about that," said Anushka. "How are you all doing? I was just sorting out the prize. All the pugs look incredible in their outfits."

I wandered away. Anushka had made a friend and it was all because of me. That's Puggy Power!

After catching up with all my friends, swapping scents and sniffing ears and bottoms, I spotted a stranger approaching us.

"Who's Anushka?" he asked, checking his notepad.

Anushka hesitantly raised her hand.

"Ah, okay, right," he said. "I'm George, the photographer, here from the Guildford Gazette to take the photos of today's event. Can you all gather together, please, for a picture?"

There was a buzz around everyone as our humans scooped up their dogs or put them down on the grass. Some of the camera-loving pugs had already lolled their tongues for their moment in the spotlight. Daisy's curly tail twirled around while she stood still, giving her best gooey eyes, while Pearl sat upright, like the lady she was, in her best girly regal pose. Sherlock did his best, tilting his head in the direction where he thought the camera was, while Doug peacefully sat down to allow the other more gregarious pugs to have their moment.

Everyone had settled down into their positions when all of a sudden an almighty sound of a raspberry emerged from Henry. His chops wobbled as we all turned to see whose bottom had burped.

But Henry didn't want to admit it was him. "What?" he growled deeply to Percy. "Was that you?"

Anushka picked me up, so I told her how much I loved her as I hadn't done so since we arrived.

The man waved his arms and asked people to stand in a line. Then he stood back and held up the thing around his neck. He squinted into it but shook his head. It looked like something disappointed him.

"Ah, it's hard, innit, to get a good shot of a pug, ugly buggers," he said, wrinkling his nose as he looked up and then back into his camera. He asked for all of us to be put down on the ground and then turned the big eye on his neck towards me. Then, he shook his head again and took one of Daisy and then Sherlock.

Daisy knew what to do. She cocked her head with a face so sweet that I longed to run over and lick it. Sherlock gurned into the camera, the best way he could.

"Oh blimey, there's not a good-looking one among you." The man shrugged. "Even with this many to choose from."

A grumble swept over our humans, as pugs were swept up for appreciative cuddles. They didn't like what the man had said and felt protective.

"Where's my cuddle?" I woofed to Anushka, hopping from paw to paw for attention, but she was talking to the man.

"Have you got everything you need now?" she asked, with a serious tone in her voice.

"Guess this will have to do," said the grumpy man.

"Er, we don't think our dogs are ugly, by the way!" Anushka was laughing, but I could tell that she was cross.

The man grumbled again. He took a few more photographs, and said he'd make do with what he had. By the time he left, all of the humans were chatting more than ever. The grumpy man had bonded us all together as everyone agreed on one thing.

Our humans all love us very much, thank you. Pugs are the best! And nobody can ever tell us we're ugly!

"This is The Best Day Ever," I snuffled, racing around again in a zoomie.

Soon afterwards, A Man Called James handed out a prize of a toy pug to Sherlock. I watched enviously when the toy bypassed Sherlock's drooling lips to go into his owner's bag. Couldn't blame him for wanting to get his teeth into it. I bet it smelled of me too. Lucky him!

Like all good days, it was over far too quickly. I checked Anushka was okay as she said goodbye to everyone. I was so happy she'd made as many friends as me. I bet she felt really puggy that day. Wahoo!

On the way home, Anushka seemed very tired, so I let her stop more than usual to watch me sniff and pee. I'm pretty sure she also thought this was The Best Day Ever, but with humans you can't always tell.

*

Donkey is my best friend in bed. Even if he makes me drool, I won't chew him too much. He likes me to snuggle him when nobody is in our house. He agrees with everything I say, never interrupts and has the same look on his face whether he's happy or sad. He watches me eat my dinner, but never asks to share. He loves me.

Everyone needs a Donkey in their life.

When I woke up from my snoozle, stretched and had my biscuits, everything was being tidied away, including Donkey.

Anushka buzzed around the flat until it didn't look like where we lived any more. Then finally, when everything was cleared away, she looked satisfied.

"Your mum and dad won't be judging how tidy this place is," A Man Called James said.

Anushka smiled in a way she does when she doesn't agree.

After dinner, we were enjoying a snuggle when I realised Anushka sounded offended. "Oh, Bertie…" she said.

I opened one eye. "Huh?"

"Oh Bertie, please don't blow off like that when my mum and dad come." Anushka groaned, clutching her nose.

"What?" I snorted. "I was only relaxing!"

Anushka continued to tidy up a few more things, including my bed, which looked so neat that I longed to make a new nest from it. And then *finally* she seemed relaxed.

The finishing touches, she said, were the Christmas decorations. As she hung up string across our fireplace, she seemed back to her old happy self.

"Bertie," she laughed, "you have more cards than James and me! Look, you have 20 and we just have three. What a popular little pug you are."

I knew everyone loved me from The Park. Why was this news to her? But I was happy she was happy, and when she let me chew one of the empty envelopes it felt like The Best Day Ever.

Afterwards, the Christmas tree went up, with sparkly bits I wasn't allowed to touch. I say a tree, but it didn't smell like one. When I cocked my leg to make it more realistic, A Man Called James leapt from the sofa as if it was on fire.

"Okay," I woofed. I made a mental note. The Silver Book, the tree, newspapers… All things to sniff when nobody was looking.

*

The next morning, I woke up super early and bounced on my bed.

"Urrr, it's 5am," moaned A Man Called James. "You don't even believe in Santa. You're a pug."

Anushka laughed. "If Santa was real, he'd definitely give Bertie a big present," she said. "What would you like, boy? A giant-sized Gravy Bone? Yasss please, Mummy!"

I snorted. I loved it when my human put on her puggy voice.

I needed a pee, but could also sense something exciting and nervous was happening. And I was right.

Anushka handed me a long, red sock that she let me snuffle into. I ripped open a few dog treats. Then, after drinking her black stuff, she quickly filled the flat with the smell of meat and potatoes. She kept checking the clock. The clock is always important to the humans, but today it seemed especially so.

The doorbell rang, and in trooped Anushka's people. Her mum and dad ruffled my head briefly before sitting down. Suddenly, our flat felt very small, and Anushka's heartbeat seemed louder than usual.

"Relax," I barked. "We have meat and roast potatoes. And… wait for it… sausages wrapped in bacon!"

Anushka asked me to shhh, before glancing at her parents. She had a strange look on her face, but I could tell they loved dogs. Her dad knew exactly which bit to scratch. He could even give a good "chinny", something humans only know if they understand how we love to rest our chins on their knee for a fuss. How did he know? Maybe Anushka told him.

At last, the delicious food was brought out to its second-to-last destination. The human's plate. And then it made its way into my mouth, as titbits were dropped down for me.

I managed to give enough gooey eyes to earn myself 17 mouthfuls of Christmas dinner. Pigs in blankets are my Favourite Things Ever now. Even Donkey agreed, and he didn't get any.

All seemed good for everyone, except I felt that something was bothering Anushka.

"Honestly, everyone is having a good time," soothed A Man Called James in a quiet voice, when they took the plates back into the kitchen. "Your mum and dad are getting on really well. We're all going to see your sister and family tomorrow at hers. Just relax."

Anushka sighed. "I just think Dad seems a bit quiet. I hope Mum enjoyed the food. I know she prefers rice."

I went back into the living room where her parents were also talking.

"Anushka made a lovely meal, didn't she?" her dad said. "I think she worries too much, though. Wish we could do more to help."

"Oh yes, dinner was lovely," her mum agreed, "but don't say anything as we don't want to cause any offence."

By the time dinner was over, I lay on my bed, belly hanging out. I didn't even need to dream of Gravy Bones. Too full to move, I almost missed everyone saying goodbye.

I only just saw them out at the door. Anushka's mamma gave her an awkward hug while her dad briefly kissed the top of her head. There was love but also silence, and I sensed lots of unspoken words in the air.

"Thanks for a lovely lunch," her dad said. "See you soon?"

"Yes of course," Anushka said. "Let's not leave it so long next time."

"We just need to all make more effort to take the time to meet," said her mum.

Once the door closed, much to Anushka's relief, she pushed her face into my ruff. "Why do I always feel like I get something wrong, Bertie?" she asked me.

I gave her a lick until she smiled again. "You don't," I grunted. "Humans worry too much. And anyway, I still love you."

*

"January is the most miserable month of the year," grumbled A Man Called James as he carried me downstairs outside for my first pee of the day.

It didn't seem much different to me. Our flat was still warm, my food was still on time, and the duvet was still The Softest Thing Ever.

I'd been taken to a place they called Pets at Home the previous weekend to choose my own bed. They all laughed when I stood next to the one I wanted. Apparently, it was the biggest one in the entire shop, but why would I want anything less? Anushka smiled, while A Man Called James sighed and took out his money. He muttered something about me being "spoilt", but it's something every pug should be. Every dog, in fact.

I lay in the giant bed for a good hour, but decided that, no, the big bed in Anushka's bedroom was still the best, so I made that my forever bed instead. You had to try these things before deciding.

A Man Called James wasn't impressed. Anushka understood, though, and she couldn't stop laughing. My comfort is clearly of utmost importance to her too.

Back inside, Anushka got ready for work. She was going there on her own that day, so I was to wait at home, having a solo pug day.

I had my breakfast then a snoozle on the duvet, then another one on the square of sunshine on the same spot on the carpet. Then, I went back to the duvet until she came home and it was time for more cuddles and dinner. If I was lucky, the Gravy Bone dream happened at least once. If not, I snuggled Donkey and he loved me back. I longed for a chase in The Park with my friends, but Anushka seemed to think she had to do something – what she called "special" – again.

"But you *are* special!" I barked, though it went over her human head.

A few things arrived with the postman, and it took all my willpower not to rip the paper when it landed on the mat. Okay, maybe I had a little nibble but nobody said anything.

Anushka seemed to know what was inside the parcel and

opened a round piece of plastic she called a Jumping Hoop. Along with a strange piece of plastic they called a Tunnel. Anushka sat at one end and A Man Called James tried to coax me into the other end.

"Come on, come on, Bertie!" A Man Called James said, in a fake excited voice, patting the carpet.

They both looked very enthusiastic, so I cocked my head and wondered what was so fascinating looking down the tube. I had a little sniff and couldn't work it out, so I just watched them continue to smile weirdly.

"Go on, Bertie!"

"You can do it!"

"Do what?" I woofed in confusion, running in a zoomie circle.

I couldn't work out what they wanted, so went and lay down on my own bed. I'd no idea what power this tube had over them, but it wasn't for me.

Anushka followed me and sounded a bit upset. "Oh dear, maybe I should get something other than an obstacle course for the next pug meet up," she said. "I've seen one of those see-saw planks that dogs can walk up and down too. Look, I just want pugs and owners to have fun. It's not like they're coming for my sparkling conversation, is it?"

She showed A Man Called James something on the Silver Book, but he shook his head.

"Anushka, you don't need to be spending £200 on a see-saw for dogs," he said. "It's only a meet up in a local park." He wrapped his arms around her, so I stomped my feet to ask to join in. He sighed and lifted me up, and I licked Anushka's face.

"People just want to meet up and make friends," he said. "A mini obstacle course is all most pugs will manage. I'm sure the tunnel, a hoop and a few hurdles will be fine. Try not to worry. Bertie will find it fun, won't you?"

I lolled my tongue and barked. Of course I would! Just leave the tunnel out of it.

"And see? Bertie loves your sparkling conversation," A Man Called James said.

CHAPTER 6

Anushka

"Bruce prefers humans to other pugs," a pug owner called Hannah said to Anushka. "Just like some of us humans prefer dogs."

Hannah, a woman in her 40s, smiled awkwardly after offering to help Anushka set up the tunnel and bollards. A bonus of the day was getting to know a few of the lovely owners and their memorable dogs, such as Bruce, the biggest and shyest pug Anushka had come across.

Hannah had a hesitant manner, and Bruce seemed to mirror her demeanour around other pugs, eyeing them with large, cautious eyes. Anushka felt herself relax. This social occasion clearly wasn't easy for either of them, and already they felt like kindred spirits.

"I can relate to Bruce, despite having arranged today myself." Anushka laughed. "Still, we're all here now, so well done to us."

Hannah's face relaxed while she bent down to give Bruce a reassuring pat on the head.

As they chatted about other doggy events they'd seen advertised but never attended, a young man appeared at their side with a reporter's notebook.

"Simon from the Guildford Gazette," he said. "Anushka?"

Anushka was baffled for a moment, but then remembered who he was. "Oh yes, of course," she said. "You messaged me a few weeks ago. Okie-dokes, yes. Do you still want a photo?"

"Actually, we'd like to do a video this time," Simon said with an apologetic air. "Our readers, I mean, viewers, it's all online these days, isn't it, go nuts for anything pet-wise. My editor loves it. Click rates skyrocket. Especially when it comes to dogs doing stupid, I mean funny, things."

By chance, they all looked at Bruce, who looked up as if to say "who, me?", before he glanced at the tunnel and made a snorting sound that only meant one thing.

Not on your nelly!

"Well, I'm sure we can find an enthusiastic pug to take part," Anushka said, brightly, reading the pug's mind. "Let me just ask around quickly."

She nipped away to tentatively approach owners, who were chatting in circles, while Hannah was left with Simon.

"Goodness, it's popular this event, isn't it?" he said, rocking on his heels. "Not seen a park in Guildford so busy since the Golden Jubilee."

"It's nice to be invited somewhere where your dog is welcome too," Hannah agreed. "Bruce is like my shadow. Comes everywhere with me. Don't you, Bruce?"

Bruce lolled out his tongue in recognition.

A pair of pugs appeared as if volunteering themselves to have a go. They both waddled over like two middle-aged men with broad shoulders in too-tight-fitting jeans. Both of them had a permanent frown and downturned jowls, with eyes that glanced suspiciously from side to side. They were a funny duo and reminded Hannah of Phil and Grant Mitchell from *EastEnders*.

"Oooh, are you lads going to have a run through the tunnel?" Simon asked, bending down to pug eye level.

One pug's lower jaw jutted out as he promptly cocked a leg.

"Hey, stop," cried Anushka from a few metres away. She dashed over, waving her hands. The pug paused mid-leg cock, gave a desultory sniff and ran off.

Anushka recognised the dogs as Henry and Percy. They belonged to a slim strawberry blonde lady who stood at the edge of the circle. She made a mental note to go and say hello to her as the dogs bounded back over like a pair of bouncers protecting their owner.

"Okay, are there any volunteers for the obstacle course?" James shouted, loudly.

Kandeece, a pretty young woman with auburn hair, holding a pug with an unfocused look in his eye, stepped forward. "Sherlock will have a bash." She smiled. "Probably quite literally, as he's blind."

Anushka was about to ask about this, when a blonde lady holding two sweet-faced girl pugs walked up.

"My girls Daisy and Lilly will have a go too," Kelly W grinned.

"Wonderful," Anushka said, clapping her hands. "Come on then, pugs, let's go!"

Simon held up his camera, ready to capture the golden moment on film. But as Kandeece and Kelly W cajoled their dogs from the other side of the tunnel, all of the pugs, including Bertie who'd dashed over to see what the fuss was about, collectively stood still. As if they'd had words – as if the pugs agreed collectively they weren't to be humiliated. *Especially* if the Guildford Gazette was there to capture it.

As minutes ticked by, Anushka felt her neck beginning to turn hot and red. She pulled off her scarf and crouched down to plead with the dogs directly.

"Oh, come on, puggies," she said with desperation. Suddenly, an obstacle course felt like the worst idea in the world and she wanted the grass to open and swallow her up. "Right, anyone else think their pug can do it? First one around gets a biscuit."

Bertie cocked his head at one of his favourite words. But sensing more pugs arriving, he ran off to greet them.

Anushka began stammering an apology for wasting the reporter's time when one of the pugaliers broke ranks. With a bit of coaxing from his owner, he zoomed around the course while the owner clapped encouragingly. By the time the pug shot through the tunnel, applause had broken out, followed by cheering as if he'd won Crufts.

"Got the film, thanks," Simon said. "That'll give advertisers a boost come Monday morning. Especially if we do it in slow-mo, and add something like *Chariots of Fire* as the soundtrack."

*

Back at the flat, Anushka shoved all of the obstacle course paraphernalia into the back of the downstairs cupboard. Once she found enough time, she'd take it to the tip. She was glad that James had stopped her from spending more money on the see-saw for dogs.

On the way home, she'd made a mental decision to leave event planning to the experts. Instead, she was going to keep up Bertie's Facebook page and leave her own socialising strictly online.

As lovely as her conversations with owners had been, she'd decided there was no need for big group meetings. And, definitely, no need for her to be arranging them.

Later on, while flicking idly through the channels on the TV, James turned to Anushka. "So which pug owners did you get chatting to today?" he asked. Anushka spotted a glint of enthusiasm in his eyes that she'd never noticed before. "I got to know Kelly P, the owner of Miss Pearly Pug, and Vicky, whose boys Henry and Percy followed her like a pair of bouncers." James chuckled. "What's interesting is so many people from such a variety of walks of life have a pug," he said. "Not often you meet a beautician, a lawyer, a banker and a former West End dancer all in the same park on a drizzly Sunday. Pugs really do have broad appeal."

Anushka felt a stab of guilt. James was, by far, the more outgoing of the two of them, and she wondered if he'd like to have more of a fun social life. Fun to Anushka was staying in to watch TV and snuggle with Bertie.

"West End dancer?" she said. "Who was that?"

"Henry and Percy's owner, Vicky," James replied. "She didn't have time to tell me her whole story but she'd suffered from an illness so had to give up her dream job dancing on the stage with the likes of Matthew Kelly. Her pugs really helped her through it. Did you get to chat much to any of the others?"

Anushka thought about her own conversations. There was Hannah, who later told her that Bruce had become like a surrogate partner after her 24-year marriage had ended. Bruce was a real character, a deeply shy awkward pug, which was a shame considering how much attention he attracted due to his very large size. Hannah believed that if he could speak he'd sound like Scooby Doo, something that made Anushka give a belly laugh.

Then there was Miss Pearly Pug, who waggled her hips and tail into the crowd. Anushka already followed her on Instagram, so it felt like a mini-celebrity had arrived. She didn't disappoint, dressed in a luxurious metallic sweater with a Chanel-esque bouclé harness and matching beret, despite the muddy grass. Her owner, Kelly P, not to be confused with Kelly W, Daisy and Lilly's mum, was very friendly too.

During a lull in conversation with the owners, Anushka found herself rooted to the spot. As a reluctant group leader, she wasn't sure whether to circulate or leave people to it. So many people seemed to be making friends already, and Anushka wasn't sure where to put herself, until Kandeece came over.

"Your Bertie is keen to hang out with my Sherlock," she'd said. "Look at them go. You wouldn't know he's blind, would you?"

Anushka had been amazed. Sherlock had no trouble keeping up with Bertie's game of running in a circle. He seemed to know exactly which end to sniff too.

"Blind?" Anushka had asked. "Was this from birth?"

Kandeece had taken a deep breath, before launching into a story that she still found painful to recall. "Yes," she had explained. "I'd spotted an advert on Pets4Homes from a breeder who'd bluntly said the pug puppy would be destroyed if a home wasn't found for him that very day."

Anushka's eyes had widened in horror. She'd never heard of such cruelty. She gazed down at Sherlock, who was running around with Bertie without a care in the world. Already, she was pleased he'd found an owner like Kandeece, who clearly idolised him.

"I'd never bought a pedigree dog before," Kandeece had continued. "But I went along to see the breeder, who, despite the advert, was actually registered with the Kennel Club. Sherlock's mum was clearly very tired and looked worn out. I didn't know at the time, but it's a sign of being overbred."

Anushka had nodded. "Well, when it's all new to you, it's hard to know what to look out for."

Kandeece had swallowed hard as she continued with her story. "I fell in love with Sherlock the moment I saw him, but when we got him home I instantly knew something was wrong. He couldn't walk in a straight line and seemed confused. We took him straight to a vet and an X-ray revealed a fractured skull. Poor Sherlock had been beaten so badly that part of his skull was crushed. That night, he had a brain scan and then an operation. He miraculously survived."

Wiping a tear from her eye, Anushka had put a hand on Kandeece's arm to comfort her.

"I felt so angry for Sherlock," Kandeece had admitted. "I immediately reported the breeder to the police, and the Kennel Club too, but nobody took any action. Can you believe it?"

"What a start in life," Anushka had said, sadly. She'd genuinely felt shocked. "How can people treat a puppy like that?"

As if he'd guessed people were talking about him, Sherlock had dashed over.

"How does he know you're here if he can't see?" Anushka had asked.

"He's got an incredible sense of smell," Kandeece had said. "He manages his condition so well and, if he bumps into something, he shrugs it off and tries again."

"What a great philosophy for life," Anushka had mused.

She recounted a few of these stories to James, who listened intently.

"Sounds like you got to know several of the owners, Anushka," he said. "That's fantastic." He slid his hand into hers and tightened his grip.

Bertie sensed the moment and stirred from his nap next to them. He opened one eye and began licking Anushka.

"I'm proud you've done this," James said. "Only a few months ago, you would have struggled to make much conversation with our neighbours. To think you've *arranged* a whole social event for lots of people is... well... very impressive."

Anushka laughed it off. At the end of the meet up, several owners had enthusiastically asked when the next one would be, but she didn't know how to reply. Accidentally, she'd become a group leader, a role she wasn't exactly comfortable continuing with.

It was also midwinter, the weather was terrible and everyone owned a breed of dog that loathed the rain. So Anushka tried to make a joke about struggling to find a gazebo big enough to hire, and said everyone should check out the Facebook page. She needed to buy herself some time to think about the plan, if there was to be one.

"So when's the next pug extravaganza?" James teased.

"Don't hold your breath." Anushka laughed as Bertie licked her cheek.

*

A few weekends later, Anushka walked down the cobbled roads of Guildford High Street with Bertie on his lead, while she pulled up her coat collar against the relentless bitter nip in the air. She kept her head down, only glancing up to look at the rolling Surrey Hills, with trees like bare sticks against a Tupperware-coloured sky.

Not able to imagine it ever turning to spring again, Anushka shivered and was glad she'd put a little coat onto Bertie. Winter felt like this every year. Never-ending. *Right now*, she thought, *a coffee would be welcome.*

Just as she crossed the road, a sign for a new cafe caught her eye. Esquires Coffee made a welcome change from the usual Starbucks/Costa franchises. Decked out with funky industrial décor, it had cool steel lamps overhead and a long glass counter filled with delicious-looking pastries and cakes.

The busy tables inside revealed many new customers were as intrigued as Anushka. Bertie tugged impatiently on his lead as if he wanted to go in.

Anushka rarely went into a cafe on her own, except to buy a speedy coffee and leave. Very occasionally, at the weekend, she would sit with a book in Starbucks if James was out with friends.

This place looked as if it attracted young mums and people working on laptops. People who wanted to sit leisurely inside. They probably didn't even do takeaways. Small spits of rain began to splatter onto the window as Anushka and Bertie gazed in. A cold draught made the back of her neck shiver, so she pulled up her collar again while Bertie strained at the lead. Sometimes, it felt as if he was taking her for a walk, and not the other way around.

Allowing Bertie to lead the way, Anushka pushed at the heavy glass door. The blast of warm air inside, along with the sweet aroma of freshly baked bread and cookies, was most welcome. As was the smile of the friendly lady behind the counter.

"What can I get you?" she asked.

Anushka didn't look at the menu because she'd only eaten breakfast an hour earlier. But now she was here, she realised she could do with her usual hit of caffeine. And the croissants did look most tempting.

"A cappuccino, please," she said. "And go on, then, a pain au chocolat too."

"Coming right up." The lady grinned. "Oh… who is this handsome boy?"

As usual, Bertie was lolling his tongue out at the stranger. The never-ending prospect of some fuss, especially from a dog lover, was something he had a sixth sense for.

"His name's Bertie," said Anushka, smiling with pride. It never ceased to amaze her what little magnets these dogs were.

The lady came out from behind the counter to rub his head and ears. "Oooh, I think I might have something for you, Bertie, in a minute," she said. "Go and sit down and I'll bring your coffee over."

Anushka chose the table nearest to her and plopped Bertie onto her lap. At times like this, he felt like a comfort blanket.

The lady brought over a drink, as a group of mums with buggies came inside. Anushka could hear the couple of girl-friends chatting in a conspiratorial way behind her.

"He never said that."

"Oh. My. God."

"Really?"

"Yeah, and then…"

Anushka pulled out her phone from her pocket to idly scroll through it. The friends talked as if they'd known each other from their school days. As she stared at the never-ending items on Instagram adverts, Anushka thought about how much fun it would be to be a part of that conversation.

The familiar hot sense of awkwardness washed over her as she flicked over to Facebook. A few messages popped up on Bertie's Facebook page, so she clicked them open.

Hi Anushka, I just wanted to say thanks so much for arranging such a lovely meet up in the park. I didn't have the chance to come and say hi, but it was lovely to meet other pug owners. I'm Vicky and my pugs are Henry and Percy. The meet up in the park was the first chance for me to socialise properly since I fell unwell a year ago. Anyway, I am not writing to make you feel sorry for me, it's more of a thank you for sorting something so fun and relaxed. Seeing Henry and Percy enjoy themselves gave me such a boost. I did chat to a couple of the owners but hopefully I'll come and say hi to you next time. Vicky.

Anushka sat back in her chair, touched. She remembered now. The quiet, pretty, blonde lady who had hung around the back of the group. James had said hello to her briefly and she'd told him all about being a West End dancer.

Vicky's challenging situation put her own social phobias into perspective. How brave she was to go out and about, learning to re-live life with a disability. Anushka didn't know if she'd have been strong enough to do the same.

As she sat looking at her phone, another Facebook post popped up.

We're all desperate to get to know Bertie… when is the next Pug Meet Up? If we want to get out of the rain, maybe we can go to a cafe next time? Love Miss Pearly the Pug.

The cafe owner tapped Anushka on the shoulder. "Would your lovely dog like a dog treat?" She smiled, waving a small bone-shaped biscuit. She didn't need to ask twice, as Bertie gave her his best liquid-brown saucer eyes.

"I think you have your answer." Anushka smiled.

The cafe manager crouched down for Bertie to gobble up the biscuit. "There you go, fella," she said. "Welcome to my new cafe. Hope to see you again soon."

As Bertie gobbled up the biscuit, the manager gazed at him with the true sense of affection that only a real dog lover could muster. Before Anushka had a chance to even fully formulate the idea in her head, she blurted out a question that surprised even her.

"Um, sorry if this is a strange request," she asked in a gabble. "But would you mind if a few pugs came into the cafe for a meet up? We've met in the park, but if it rains we may need somewhere inside." As soon as the words left her mouth, she wondered what on earth she was thinking. What sane business manager would want their premises overrun by excitable dogs?

Just as Anushka was about to mumble an apology, the lady's face broke into a big smile. "Oh, that sounds like something a bit different," she said. "Come on over to the till and I'll take a few details from you. I'm Nicci. When would you like to book? I think we have space in the diary in a few weeks if that's any good?"

CHAPTER 7

Bertie

Lovely Biscuit Lady glanced down at me as if she was itching to stroke me. And who could blame her? I danced around from foot to foot with my tongue out. Irresistible me!

As if she'd tapped into my puggy mind, Lovely Biscuit Lady reached to ruffle my fur.

"A meeting of pugs sounds like a wonderful idea," she said to Anushka. "Would you like me to bake some special doggie treats for the event?"

The word "treat" made me sit up straight. Anushka noticed and laughed. A second biscuit within a few minutes? This was turning into The Best Day Ever.

"Sounds wonderful," Anushka said. "Bertie certainly approves."

The two of them chit-chatted back and forth for a while.

When we walked outside afterwards, Anushka's hand held her lead tighter. "What have I gone and done, Bertie?" she said softly. "It's all very well arranging a meeting outside in a park, but there's so much more to think about in a cafe, isn't there?"

That night, I could feel Anushka tossing and turning in my bed. I tried to lie closer to calm her, but her legs moved more than A Man Called James's did. During the day, she also spent long hours glued to her Silver Book, typing. I wanted to help her but had no idea how.

So I sat and listened and followed her around the house while she wrote on pieces of paper and made phone calls. Instinctively, I knew Anushka needed more pug love than ever over the next few weeks, so I made sure I reminded her more than usual.

I love you. I am here for you. I. Love. You.

*

All of us pugs know humans are obsessed with time. They look at their screen or the face on the wall and leap up or run about because they have to be somewhere. To pugs, the only times that matter are home time, dinner time, walk time and treat time. But humans talk about days or weeks or months.

Some time later – no idea how long this was – I watched as their eyes widened over the Silver Book. It seemed like something exciting was actually happening. Anushka explained to James that she was going to call it the Pop Up Pug Cafe and it was all for me and my new friends. But as if that wasn't enough, something else caused much human excitement too.

"Oh my God, James," cried Anushka. "Look! The pug meet up at the cafe has made *The Daily Telegraph*!"

All was revealed when they brought home another fresh and crisp newspaper to make my chops drool. They were keeping it well away from me, like the Silver Book, and pored over it as if it was a precious map that could reveal the whereabouts of the juiciest bone.

"James, read this," said Anushka.

"The unfashionable Surrey town of Guildford is the unlikely location for the UK's latest hipster haunt: The Pop Up Pug Cafe..." he read aloud. "Organised in collaboration with the Guildford Pug Meet Up group, the local cafe will host pugs and their owners in what the organisers have described ambitiously as 'the event of the century'."

"I put that on the page as a little joke," said Anushka. "Carry on."

James continued, "Unfortunately, the event is fully booked for now. But there is a waiting list and, given its success, the possibility of a follow-up, or perhaps a plucky entrepreneur in Shoreditch will steal the idea."

"Oooh, I hope nobody steals the idea of our Pop Up Pug Cafe." Anushka laughed. "I'm not sure it really will sell out, but this is great publicity, isn't it?"

After another long, busy day of snoozing, a whizz around The Park and two dreams of Gravy Bones, it was the evening yet again. The best hour was the snuggle on the sofa with the best human in the world. But, as I tilted my head for another chinny, Anushka's screen made a ping sound and she let out a scream. Then she cried out in a way worthy of a good dog howl.

"Wassup?" I barked, eager to know more.

"James!" she called out. "In total, there are 360 people interested in coming to the Pop Up Pug Cafe. People are coming from all over the country too – even from London!"

I stood up. This was big news in the Fernando household, I could tell. I tilted my head so they knew I understood, but nobody was looking at me.

A Man Called James usually has a calm face but even his eyebrows shot up to his hairline. "Wow, Anushka. I know I said there was a gap in the market, but…" He sank down onto the sofa to stare into the Silver Book that Anushka had flicked on. "The article calling Guildford 'unfashionable' has caused a bit of a storm, hasn't it." He laughed. "People feel rather affronted. Too right, as well. We've even got a trendy new cafe on the high street now, don't you know, along with the world's first pug cafe!"

Anushka's eyes were shining. I only usually saw this face when she was staring into my eyes or deciding which cake to choose from a cafe.

"Okay, we can do this," she said. "Er, I'll need to let Nicci know. What else? Oh yes. Tables! We'll have to make sure there's enough of them. See if we can get extra chairs in too. Oh my God, there's only capacity for 40 people at a time so we'll need to allocate time slots. Oh, and dog treats. We have to make sure there's enough to go around for all the pugs coming. I want to ask for everyone's names so we can welcome them with a puguccino."

"Puguccino?" asked James.

"Yes!" Anushka laughed. "A beverage of cream in a cup especially for pugs. They can't have their own cafe without their own drink."

I waited patiently until she finished her human excitement before asking for my cuddle. Finally, she scooped me up and squeezed my face into hers.

"I love you," I snuffled. I licked her as hard as I could, imagining all the new faces to lick, both humans and pugs. This was going to be The Best Cafe Ever!

"This is going to be the best cafe ever," Anushka said, putting on her deep pug voice as she tried to imagine what

I was thinking. "And I'm going to make loads of pug friends over the nicest biscuits."

And in this case, you know, I knew she was gonna be right!

*

"What if something goes wrong?" Anushka said to James a while later. "I don't know… what if a pug gets scalded by hot coffee? Or one runs off out of the cafe? It's not a kennel, is it? It's a cafe. They're not designed for small dogs, are they?"

"But equally, what if everything goes right?" he replied. "Look, don't think about doing it for yourself, Anushka. Do it for Bertie. He's going to love it."

I snorted with approval, and the sound made my human smile. Success! I circled her with a quick lap of celebration.

Later on, we drove in our car to the cafe on the high street. The cafe was empty, but Nicci, the kind-faced lady, was waiting for us with a big smile. She was keen to show us some munchies behind the counter that drove my nose wild.

"We have barkscotti instead of biscotti," she said. "And pugcakes. All made with dog-friendly ingredients. And this is your pièce de résistance – a puguccino!"

Anushka seemed as delighted as if they were for her. I knew she'd made this drink up herself. "Puguccinos are special because they're especially for dogs," she told me. "Why can't pugs have a drink just for them in a coffee shop?" She wrote the names of the pugs coming that day on the front of the cups in her best handwriting. Too right. Much nicer than the black stuff as well.

The. Best. Day. Ever.

Anushka looked more relaxed as she opened the box she'd been preparing and pulled out small triangles with my face on and a poster of my beautiful face. Then she climbed up a ladder to fix some of these to the ceiling. I barked with approval, circling her ladder so many times that Nicci eventually shooed me away.

Anushka and A Man Called James stood back, admiring my faces that were fluttering between the walls. Then, Nicci came in with a tray of little paper cups that made my nose tickle with anticipation. Something sweet, creamy and delicious was coming right up.

"The first puguccino goes to Bertie," Nicci said to A Man Called James. "In a cup, it's the perfect size for every pug nose. I thought we'd give all our four-legged guests one for free on arrival."

A Man Called James took one and knelt down to offer it to me. I didn't hesitate to dive in, licking the floaty creaminess so fast that I had plenty of splashes to savour with numerous licks of my nose. The humans all looked at me, very pleased.

"I think Bertie gives it the paws up." Anushka laughed.

The bell on the cafe door rang. It was time for my friends to arrive. Daisy, Lilly, Pearl, Sherlock, Bruce, Henry and Percy all bounded in with their humans.

"Can we let our dogs off the lead?" someone asked.

"Absolutely," said Anushka. "We've made the cafe as dog-friendly and safe as possible. Welcome to the Pop Up Pug Cafe."

Both Sherlock and Daisy paused briefly to check their humans were okay to be allowed off their leads, before dancing in circles to celebrate. I went to join them. In this smaller vicinity, I had a better smell from Sherlock. He'd had a lot of sadness, and I could tell his head was a funny shape, but he also had a great sense of humour, sniffing everyone and shaking his head as if their smell confused him.

Sherlock and Daisy's humans were smiling as they went over to Anushka. Behind them, more and more pugs and their humans walked in. A Man Called James stood at the door to say hello to everyone, like a pug door man.

"This looks incredible!" Kandeece cried. "You've transformed this place into a mecca for pugs."

"I agree," said Kelly W, Daisy and Lilly's owner. "It's such a clever idea."

I could sense Anushka's heart swell as she smiled with relief. "It's all for the pugs." She shrugged. "And of course,

Bertie helped me no end. Didn't you, Bertie?" I tilted my head as she put on her adorable deep voice that she thinks sounds just like me. "Yass, I did, Mummy!" she growled. "It was all my idea, really."

I love my human but she's too modest.

*

I watched in wonder as Anushka relaxed when she sat down to chat to Kandeece and Kelly W. "Is Sherlock going to be okay inside a smaller area with so many pugs?" she asked Kandeece, nervously.

"Oh yes," replied Kandeece. "Nothing stops him."

As if to prove a point, Sherlock ran in laps around a nearby table, almost sending Nicci flying as she came in with another tray of puguccinos. While we'd been chatting, this place had been filling up with more pugs than I'd ever seen in one cafe.

I ran over to Sherlock to sniff his face. He stared back at me, looking slightly over my shoulder, but I quickly realised he wasn't looking at my eyes. Or the munchies behind the glass counter. He was staring into the unknown, but laughing with it.

"You can't see me, can you?" I snorted.

"Nope," he snuffled. "I'm blind. But nothing stops me."

As if in sync, his human told everyone to watch as she chucked a piece of barkscotti in our direction. Sherlock turned in a flash and snapped the treat between his teeth. Then, he raised his snout into the air like he was gripped in a trance and bolted like lightning behind the counter to the kitchen.

"Come back, Sherlock!" Kandeece shouted.

Anushka looked alarmed. I could sense her adrenaline was sky-high, as she followed Sherlock and Kandeece into the cafe kitchen. Bruce, who always hung back from our group, immediately moved faster than I'd ever seen him. The prospect of an extra treat was too tempting for him too!

We all stood behind Sherlock, who barked by the fridge as if there was a cat trapped inside.

"What's going on?" I woofed.

"Bertie, there's cheese in there, that's what," he whimpered with drooling chops. "I can smell it. Cheeeeese!"

"Cheese?" I snorted. I couldn't smell a thing. But if there was some inside, I wasn't going to miss out.

Kandeece grabbed Sherlock off the floor. She turned to apologise to Anushka and Nicci, who'd followed us to see what the fuss was about. "I'm so sorry," Kandeece said, looking horrified. "Sherlock can smell cheese a mile off, even in a fridge. Everywhere he goes, even if I take him to friends' houses, he goes straight to the fridge to bark next to it for a slice."

Nicci laughed. "Well, I'm afraid we need our cheese for our toasties. Now, I have to please ask everyone to leave the kitchen. It's against health and safety to have customers or, er, pugs in the back of the cafe."

Anushka apologised as Kandeece took Sherlock and Bruce back into the cafe. I trotted after them. I couldn't stop thinking about cheese myself now.

*

Back inside the customer area, more pugs joined us. There was Doug with his human Cate, and Kelly P with Pearl who dashed over to join Daisy and Lilly, her best gal friends. I woofed a quick hello, but wanted to ask Sherlock something first.

"If you could smell that cheese from the inside of a fridge, you must have a super-powered snozzle," I woofed. I pushed my face into his. I suddenly needed him to know I loved him.

"Oi," he barked. "You know I need a bit of space too. I may be blind but I'm not daft."

"Sorry!" I grunted. "Is everything really pitch dark for you like it's night-time?"

"Yes, it is," he barked. "But I make up for it with smell and sound. It's more powerful since I lost my sight."

We all know dogs win paws down when it comes to our senses. Some say our sense of smell is a million times better than humans. We can smell when someone's frightened, and when they're happy. Just one sniff of dog pee tells me everything I need to know about their identity. We can even smell cancer or when there's about to be an earthquake, Anushka once told me, after watching something on their light box.

"Sherlock," I snorted. "Please teach me to smell as well as you do!"

He grinned. "You sure?"

"Go for it!" I yapped, keeping my eyes firmly shut.

Sherlock asked me to follow him to a quieter area underneath a table.

"You need to summon all your Puggy Power," he growled slowly when we sat down. "Breathe in deeply though your nostrils and imagine 'tasting' your smell."

This all seemed a bit deep to me, and Sherlock looked as if he was in some trance-like state. But I did as he said.

"Concentrate," he woofed when I opened one eye.

Already there were overwhelming smells from everywhere. Sweat and scents from the dogs and their owners. I could even smell Anushka's adrenaline from across the room, and that was without all the distracting smells of barkscotti, pugucci-nos and that godawful coffee stench.

"What am I trying to smell?" I snuffled, confused.

"Outside, across the road is a butcher's. The door opens every few minutes when a new lucky sausage buyer gets to go inside. If you concentrate, you'll be able to smell it from in here," Sherlock promised.

This was impossible. The door of our cafe only opened now and then, plus cars were going up and down the road. What was Sherlock like! But he carried on looking serious, so I closed my eyes again to focus. And then, yes, my snozzle twitched as I could just make out the whiff of a delicious sausage.

"It works!" I cried. "I have a super-powered scent like you now."

Sherlock looked very pleased with himself.

Daisy and Lilly dashed over. Daisy was the most ladylike pug I'd ever met. When Kelly W gave her a biscuit, she laid it in front of her and politely nibbled it. Couldn't imagine making anything last that long! For all her gentle manner, I could still tell who was boss. Daisy needed to give Lilly just one look and her sister would calm down.

I had a good sniff around both of them. Daisy had something else about her, but I couldn't quite pick up on it. Something didn't smell quite right, and my pug instincts tingled with worry. But she seemed cheerful enough.

What with Sherlock being blind too, I could see nothing was going to stop my newfound friends from being fabulous. As all pugs are, of course.

Daisy made my puggy heart flutter in a good way when I sat down with her. I told her all about Anushka and how I hoped she was busy making friends.

"She needed my help," I confided in Daisy, who cocked her head. She was a good listener. "It's my Puggy Purpose, you see, to help my human make friends," I snorted confidentially.

Daisy's eyes widened. "Really?" she yapped. "What's a Puggy Purpose?"

I couldn't believe she'd never heard of it before, so quickly explained, just like my Mamma had explained to me.

Daisy looked confused. "I don't think I have a Puggy Purpose," she said, doubtfully. "I mean, I know my human loves us, but I don't think I'm particularly special."

I gave her a reassuring lick. "Oh, don't you doubt yourself. You'll find one!" I barked. "If not today, then another day."

Daisy lolled out her tongue as Lilly strutted over.

"What you chatting to my sister about?" Lilly asked.

"Just making friends," I snuffled.

"You know Daisy won Britain's Top Model Pug award?" Lilly woofed at me proudly. I'd no idea what that meant, except Daisy was probably as modest as Anushka because she hadn't mentioned a thing.

Just as I was about to ask her, a hush came over everyone. Pugs and owners alike stopped what they were doing to turn to the cafe door that had just opened.

The cafe lights lowered, a spotlight came on and music began to play. It was the theme from "Stayin' Alive" by the Bee Gees. I knew this one as A Man Called James sometimes danced around the kitchen if it came on the radio. But this time, it was a pair of dude boy pugs rocking into the room.

Okay, this didn't *actually* happen, but if you imagine it did, you'd get the picture. Because two pugs in matching Hawaiian shirts walked in together as if they were timing their steps – they were clearly the coolest pugs in town.

"I'm Gizmo," woofed one. "This is my best mate, Barry."

Barry simply nodded, too cool to even woof. We all stared in awe as all the other pugs parted like a wave to let them through. So many tongues lolled out to greet them too. They already had their own fan base, and we didn't even know them!

With the confidence of a cat, Barry waggled his behind up to the cafe counter, gave one short woof and immediately grabbed Nicci's attention. Her face lit up when she saw him, and then even more so when Gizmo joined him.

"Oh my goodness, well who do we have here?" she asked.

Instinctively, she lifted them up onto the barstools by the counter. Then they were handed a puguccino each. At the same time, they dived into the cups and, with one swift lick, both of them caught all the cream from their noses.

I sensed Daisy and Lilly quiver in admiration.

"The Pug Cafe just got that little bit cooler, hasn't it?" Sherlock woofed from the corner of his mouth. "I can't see it. But I can smell style a mile off."

"Seems so," I snuffled.

Barry clicked his paw nail on the stool and Gizmo jumped down behind him like it was an unspoken instruction. They walked off together into the corner where humans automatically nudged up the couch to create a pug-sized space for them.

"Hi everyone," said Barry's human. "I'm Nicole and this is Arti, Gizmo's mum."

Anushka came forward to greet them. "They're a right pair of characters, aren't they?" she said. "Looks like the cafe is attracting all the coolest pugs in town."

All of us pugs know how special we are. But here in this little cafe off a high street in Guildford, we'd been brought together by Anushka and a set of humans who thoroughly agreed with us. Making it The Best Day Ever for us all.

CHAPTER 8

Anushka

Anushka stood at the cafe door with Bertie in her arms to wave cheerio to the last few customers and pugs. Everyone was smiling and every pug looked happily worn out. A few dogs had stray crumbs around their chops and strained at leads for a final sniff of newfound pug friends.

"Thank you for coming," Anushka said to all of them. "See you again soon."

Bertie gave a gentle woof as he watched the last of the curly tails disappear around the corner.

See you again soon? thought Anushka. *Will we?* This was an automatic polite line to say, but already she was wondering if it would happen. She gently closed the door behind her and rested her back on the cool glass. "Phew." She wanted to pinch herself. "Did others enjoy that as much as I did?"

The grin on Nicci's face reassured her. "I would say they did," Nicci said. "Here. You deserve this." She put a cup of hot chocolate with extra marshmallows and sprinkles floating on the top into Anushka's hand.

They sat down for a 10-minute break before the big tidy up began. Signs of a good time lay all around them – empty paper puguccino cups, coffee cups, plates sprinkled with crumbs of cake, streamers and stray balloons on the floor, posters of Bertie's face beaming down at them from the walls.

Despite all of the sleepless nights, fears of failure and worries about the health and safety aspects of having such a large gathering of dogs in an enclosed space, all the feedback about the Pop Up Pug Cafe had been the same.

Everyone had absolutely *loved* it.

The venue, the props, the attention to detail with the dog treats and, of course, the fun of Anushka's masterstroke, the puguccinos, had gone down like a giant plate of gravy bones with pugs and owners alike. The novelty of not only being welcomed into a cafe with your dogs, but also being encouraged to let them off the lead, wasn't lost on anyone.

"If a cafe allows you in with a dog, you feel lucky," said one owner. "If someone offers a bowl of water, it's like hitting the jackpot. But this is something else."

One lady even came to find Anushka to tell her in a near-whisper how thrilled she was. "I can finally let my inner crazy pug lady off the lead in public," she confided. "These pug people are *my* people."

Sipping her hot chocolate, Anushka was grateful it was over. But she was also glad she'd organised it.

"Maybe," Nicci teased, nudging Anushka in the ribs, "this was the first-ever dog cafe?"

Anushka laughed. In Japan, people were also pug crazy, and she knew there were already dog cafes there. But these were just petting cafes where people were allowed in to stroke pedigree dogs while sipping tea. There was also the London hipster cat cafe, with resident cats who curled up on sofas next to people using laptops. But, no, there didn't seem to be a cafe set up just for man's best friends.

"Who knows?" She grinned. "But really, Nicci, I can't thank you enough for letting us try the idea out."

James stepped down from a ladder to join them. He'd been making a start on taking down the balloons. "Did you see Bertie rubbing shoulders with the celebrity pugs?" he asked. "Barry and Gizmo have been in lots of adverts and have huge followings on Instagram."

Anushka and Nicci both giggled, recalling the charismatic pair.

"Barry had an outfit change halfway through." Anushka laughed. "He left in a hoodie."

"Some of these pugs clearly have bigger wardrobes

than I do," James said. "Were their owners as pug mad as I imagine them to be?"

Anushka had spoken to Gizmo's owner, Arti, at length and found the conversation very moving. Gizmo had been the dog for Vision Direct for the past three years. He was the pug in the red jumper and glasses that people would have seen on billboards and adverts everywhere. Anushka had asked Arti if he gave paw print autographs.

"He would do," Arti said. "But in all seriousness, he's been a little superstar in my life too." As there was a lull between customers, Anushka listened to Arti's story, transfixed.

"We bought Gizmo at the same time as we planned to start a family," Arti explained. "The idea was, we'd bring up our baby at the same as a pug. After struggling to conceive, we tried IVF. The first cycle didn't work, the second resulted in miscarriage and the third didn't go anywhere."

Arti's face clouded at the memory, and Anushka didn't know what to say. Arti took a deep breath before continuing, "We decided to hold off other cycles when we found my sister-in-law was pregnant," she said sadly. "I wanted to be there for her without me feeling awkward or going through another heartbreak, especially while it was a happier time for the family." Her eyes turned to where Gizmo was cavorting with Barry, the pair of them lapping up the attention of people taking photos with their phones.

"I'm so sorry," Anushka replied.

"That's okay," said Arti, more brightly. "Gizmo is my reason for carrying on. I haven't given up trying other avenues for starting a family either."

On a trip to Selfridges one day, a model scout had spotted Gizmo.

"He followed us around the shop and asked if he'd like to apply for a casting," Arti said. "I always thought model scouting in London was something that happened to the rich and famous, not people like us." She laughed.

She told her husband that evening about Gizmo's big chance and he laughed it off too.

"Don't be ridiculous," he said. "It must be a scam."

Regardless, Arti checked out the modelling agency, signed up and a week later found herself taking Gizmo for a photoshoot at the Mandarin Oriental Hotel in London for a major advertising campaign. Since then, Gizmo had appeared in adverts for Next, Asda, Not On The High Street and many more.

While they chatted, Gizmo trotted over as though he could tell he was the subject of their conversation. Barry followed him, along with his owner Nicole.

"Gizmo," Anushka said, stroking his head. "I'm honoured to have you at our event today." He promptly turned his back on her.

Arti laughed. "He has to be in the mood to socialise," she said. "If you put him in front of a camera, he loves to be the centre of attention. But in ordinary life, it's only when he feels like it."

Nicole joined in with the conversation to say that Barry had a similar personality. "You could say Barry is a diva," she said. "I went to puppy training classes once. The teacher told me he bullied me, as he'll only let me sit on the sofa if he feels like it. He looks down his nose at everyone, but is a softie at heart, honestly."

Barry lolled out his tongue on cue to prove her point.

Listening to all the pug talk through the afternoon, Anushka found herself sharing Bertie's own story too – about his operation and his fight back to health. Other owners, including Kelly W with her dogs Daisy and Lilly, joined them at the table.

"We held a birthday party for Bertie when he was six months old, as we didn't know if he'd make a year at the time," Anushka recalled. Everyone nodded with understanding, as they would have done the same. Their pugs were also like family to them. "Bertie's wobbly legs don't stop him from living life to the full now," she went on. Like other dogs, such as blind Sherlock, he'd beaten the odds.

All through the afternoon, Bertie disappeared for ages, making new friends, and Anushka half-wondered if he was leaving her in peace on purpose. Whenever there was a lull in her conversations though, he'd dash over, before wandering off again once a new conversation began.

"Hearing all these pug stories brings it home how special they are," said James to Nicci when she handed him a cup of coffee. Then, he recalled his own chat with Kelly W.

She'd lost her first pug, Poppy, when she'd gone in for a routine operation to be spayed. Poppy had a very rare allergic reaction to a painkiller. "It's the equivalent of a human dying from taking paracetamol," Kelly had explained. "I never planned on getting another pug afterwards. I couldn't handle the heartache in case I lost another one, but then someone needed to rehome Daisy out of the blue. She's such a doll, I couldn't resist her. Along with her sister, Lilly, they're my everything."

"Did you speak to Cate who owns Doug the pug?" asked Nicci. "He even works as a healing dog!"

Anushka nodded. She'd spoken to Cate too. Until then, she'd never heard of pugs being used to help people who needed it the most. She loved the idea.

Doug the pug volunteered with his owner Cate for a charity, Pets As Therapy. Together, they visited people in special needs schools, care homes for the elderly, and even prisons. He sat quietly next to his visitor, enabling them to confide their problems and helping to calm down shattered nerves.

Just like her pug, Cate was an older lady with a wonderfully warm, calming aura. Anushka had instantly warmed to her and they'd swapped numbers, as she did with many of the owners. By the end of the afternoon, her phone address book had doubled in size.

By the time the customers in the last allocated slot had arrived, Anushka found herself in a new rhythm. It felt surprisingly natural to welcome strangers inside and hand them a puguccino before asking, "So who do we have here?" No discerning dog owner could help but warm to a hostess who gave their pug a genuine fuss.

Each customer had their own question about the Pop Up Cafe too. "Was this cafe really just for dogs for the day?" "Could they roam anywhere they liked?" And, the most asked question of all, "Why has nobody ever come up with this idea before?"

A couple of the owners even quietly admitted they didn't get out as much as they'd like to because pugs weren't always allowed in venues.

Hannah was one of them. "I never know if Bruce is welcome in cafes and restaurants," she said. "So, we often just don't go to them. But look, he's having the time of his life." They glanced down to see Bruce sitting at Hannah's feet, drooling at the treats behind the counter. "Well, he will do once I buy him another of those delicious biscuits," she added.

There had been so many conversations, all funny and moving, and Anushka wondered if she'd ever spoken so much in one single day. She spooned the last of her melted marshmallows into her mouth, before joining Nicci to clear up the tables.

"Suddenly, it feels so empty in here without the pugs," she said.

"I don't have a dog of my own," Nicci smiled, "so it was a real treat to share our cafe with them."

*

Over the next few days, all Anushka and James wanted to natter about was the cafe. And as it turned out, so did many others. James set up a Pug Cafe Facebook page alongside Bertie's own page, and quickly it filled up with photos and messages from the other pug owners. The hashtag #pugcafe even began to appear underneath posts of pugs with cream on their nose or sitting in front of a teapot.

One morning, Anushka found herself scrolling through the latest posts on her phone in the office. For once, she allowed herself to feel pleased about something she'd done. There was no doubt that her Pop Up Pug Cafe had worked. But what would happen next? People were already asking when the next one was booked. She sighed as she fired up her computer. She had a mountain of paperwork to get through. Working as a content writer wasn't the most thrilling career, but it was a steady job that paid the bills and, after struggling to find a position to suit her, Anushka reminded herself to feel grateful for it.

As her fingers flew over the keyboard, her phone kept pinging with messages on the Facebook group. She decided she'd look at them later.

By one o'clock, she escaped down the high street among a small throng of local office workers who were relieved to swap stale office air con for sunshine and fresh air. Feeling peckish, she went into a nearby sandwich shop and joined the queue, which was already snaking out of the door. In front of her, a few people further down the queue, was a woman in dark specs with a golden Labrador guide dog. From the mutters of reassurance the woman was giving her dog, as customers squeezed past with trays of drinks and paper bags, Anushka realised the dog's name was Roger. Roger was peering over his shoulder at a group of kids trying to pull his tail.

"Won't be long, Rog," the blind lady said, patting his head.

Inside the cafe, it was a squeeze. Tables were pushed up against the wall, babies were wailing and a couple of small children flinched as Roger and his owner shuffled towards the counter. One of them started screaming when Roger glanced in his direction.

"Are dogs even allowed in here?" snapped a mum, loudly.

A hassled-looking waiter tried to walk around the lady and her dog while holding a heavy tray of boiling water and various teas. Roger stood perfectly still as another child tried to poke a lollipop into his ear.

"Madam, I am sorry," the waiter said quietly to the blind lady. "Perhaps I could serve you outside? It's rather a crush in here for the dog."

The lady gave a watery smile and turned around, with Roger carefully navigating her to the doorway.

"Mummy, I'm scared of dogs!" a child screamed.

Anushka felt like joining the lady outside herself now. It was illegal to turn a guide dog away, but she guessed the waiter was trying to be helpful. Perhaps if well-behaved dogs were allowed in places, children would feel less fearful too.

After 10 more minutes in the queue, Anushka felt hot and bothered and left empty-handed. She passed the blind lady on the street on her way out.

"Have you been served?" she asked her.

The woman's face lit up in gratitude. "The lovely young waiter has me covered, thank you."

"I'm sorry they didn't serve you inside," Anushka said. "Guide dogs should be more welcome than people, really."

"It's just life." The woman shrugged in a manner that left Anushka in no doubt that this wasn't a one-off event.

Anushka's half-hour lunch break was over in a blink of an eye, and she found herself hurrying back to her airless office all too soon, dripping with sweat. She turned down a side street where someone had placed a square plastic bowl on the floor and chalked an arrow towards it with a sign, FOR HOT DOGS.

A lovely gesture, Anushka thought, even if it *had* been left out for so long that several flies were floating on top.

*

At six o'clock that evening, after Anushka arrived home, Bertie pushed his face into hers for a solid five minutes of cuddle time on the sofa. He'd missed her! He could smell a vague whiff of Labrador on her shoes and wondered who it was. A calm old boy, he sensed, a dog well cared for.

Bertie licked Anushka's face and gave her a snuffle in a way that told her he needed a pee, so she carried him downstairs. While she waited for him to do his business at a tree, she pulled out her phone. The Pop Up Pug Cafe Facebook group had over 100 messages and around 60 new photos. She scrolled to a video with lots of love hearts.

Peering closely at the screen, she press Play. Someone had put together a professional-looking montage of the Pop Up Pug Cafe, beginning with a close-up of the poster of Bertie and then panning down to the tables with pugs everywhere below, all happily tucking into treats and licking cream-tipped noses.

Next, a pug trotted into view, pacing around a tray of puguccinos before taking a flying leap up at them. The table wobbled and the tray fell over, *You've Been Framed* style, landing on the lap of a nearby owner. The owner leapt up, only to find a crowd of pugs gathered around their legs to lick up the mess.

The owner's laughing face turned to surprise as they purposefully fell over in a comical way, landing on the floor to allow more pugs to jump on top of them. Anushka giggled uncontrollably, as this was quite adorable and funny.

She'd totally missed this happening on the day, and wondered if it had happened while she'd been restocking the treats out the back. She was glad the owner hadn't really been hurt.

But then something else grabbed her attention.

Underneath the video was a link to a major online website. Below that, someone had written in capital letters, PUG CAFÉ GOES VIRAL! There was a small write-up about the number of views.

At that moment, the front door slammed. James was home. "What's happening in the world?" he asked Anushka, noticing how absorbed she was in her phone. He planted a kiss on her lips before looking over her shoulder at the Facebook page.

"The Pop Up Pug Cafe has gone viral," she said quietly, slightly shocked.

"Eh?" James squinted over her shoulder and laughed out loud as she replayed the video. "Ahh, that's brilliant." He chuckled. "I missed that Jeremy Beadle moment."

"Hundreds of thousands of others didn't," replied Anushka. She clicked on the new website link.

He gasped. "Wow, people have watched this around the world," he said. "What? Nearly a million views!" He sat down as it sank in.

For several seconds, Anushka didn't react. She moved closer to the screen, the dancing pugs flickering in her eyes, the sounds of the laughter and music in her ears. Something special had happened here. Something unique.

Observations that one customer had made echoed in her mind. "I've never seen so many happy pugs and owners in one place! Please say you'll be back soon!"

James paused the video. "You okay, Anushka?" he asked, frowning, noticing her look of concentration.

Anushka nodded slowly. "Yes, I'm fine," she said, not mentioning that she'd just quietly made a promise to herself.

*

Anushka lay awake for hours that night while Bertie snored gently between her and James. But instead of her head being full of worries, it was filled with something else.

Plans.

Dreams.

She wanted to do this, and to do this properly – set up a cafe for pugs and work full time to make it a success. This wasn't just for Bertie, it was for all dogs. Deep down, she believed Bertie thought he deserved it. And Anushka definitely did.

Up early the next day, out with Bertie in the park, Anushka walked briskly, filling her lungs with fresh air. Somehow this felt like a new dawn, a new day. Everything was planned in her mind – now it just took action.

She drafted a resignation letter on her phone, her fingers moving deftly over the keys. She Googled "How to set up a business" and then how to trademark a name. Pop Up Pug Cafe was too much of a mouthful, so Pug Cafe it was. Her thoughts then turned to where the new cafe could be held.

She threw a ball for Bertie. Her imagination ran as excitedly as his legs while he enthusiastically trotted after it.

"Maybe we can go bigger," she said aloud to him, as she picked up the ball and lobbed it even further. "A bigger venue. More fun for pugs. In a city, even!" She thought of Brighton and how much they loved day trips there.

Bertie woofed as he shot off. Just as he had his eye on the ball, Anushka now did too.

Hours later, she emerged from her office building and squinted into bright sunshine, carrying a cardboard box containing her desk pot plant, notebooks and a hastily put-together leaving card scribbled with colleagues' names. She could hardly believe she'd had the guts to hand in her letter of resignation on a Monday, but that meant she had the rest of the week ahead of her – to set up a brand-new business officially trademarked as Pug Cafe.

CHAPTER 9

Bertie

Often when Anushka takes me for a walk, a passer-by says "hello" to me and not her. Most dogs love this! But I know my Puggy Purpose is to help Anushka to find friendship, so I always loll out my tongue and try and catch their eye. Barking "Anushka loves you too", doesn't always work. Weird! While Pug Cafe worked a treat, I still wanted more friends for her. Because my work is never done.

One Saturday, we went into town to meet her father for coffee, and Anushka told him all about the Pug Cafe idea. His face lit up when he saw me. I could tell he loved dogs from the way he gave such a good chinny rub! But there was something else I couldn't quite put my paw on. On the way home, Anushka told me all about Frazzle.

"Ahh, Bertie, I've not seen Dad fall in love with a dog since Frazzle," she said. "You would have loved him too. He was my dog when I was a little girl, and Dad's never had one since."

"He needs a new one," I woofed. It was so simple!

She didn't understand, but humans don't always get it. They worry about new dogs because they talk about "responsibility" and needing to take us for walks. Sometimes this overshadows how much love they get from us. For ever and ever.

Later, I smelled a whiff of sadness as Anushka showed A Man Called James photos from an old album containing pictures of her childhood. While A Man Called James laughed at the clothes she wore (he said she looked like an advert from the 1980s in another unfunny joke of his) and how cute she was, Anushka paused when she saw photos of her own Mamma.

If she could have reached into the photo and given her Mamma a hug, she would have done. If only they could have had a run around in The Park after a ball together. That solves everything!

When I think of my own Mamma, I have happy memories of her snuggles and sound advice. She taught me everything I needed to know as a pug.

"Remember, Bertie," she'd say, when her human lifted

her out of the cage for a sniff about outside. "We're not like other dogs. We were bred for kings. People fell in love with us so we had a responsibility to go with that."

Since she's my human, I owe Anushka all the love she's missing, and that's what I'm here to do. Seeing those family photos made me long to bring them all back together again. I wanted to see her smile like she did as a little girl.

Us dogs watch and learn when you're not looking. Since I chose Anushka to be my human, I've learnt so much about families and love.

When we go and see the mamma and father of A Man Called James, we always see my Grumpy Grandma too. She's not my real grandma, and she's called Sophie, but that's what I call her because she's definitely grumpy. She's a huge spoodle, a cross between a spaniel and a poodle.

The first time we met, I was so excited that I nearly peed on the lino floor.

"Helloooooooo," I woofed as I skidded up to her bed. But she didn't seem to hear me, so I had to go right up to her face and shout louder. "I'm Bertie, who are you? Wanna come and play? Please, please, oh come ON!"

There was a huge garden at this house. Wasting time in bed when you could be racing after bees and butterflies was silly, I told her. She growled so loudly that Anushka came running over and told her off.

"Sophie!" Anushka said, shielding me protectively. "Stop being so grumpy, Bertie is only little."

I knew Sophie meant no harm but my puggy heart sank to my paws when Sophie told me I was nothing but a rude lil pup who needed to know my place. She flexed her huge front paw as if she was itching to swat me away.

Anushka dragged me away instead. "Sophie is much older than you, Bertie," she explained to me. "She doesn't like to play, I'm afraid. Best to stay near us."

Boo to that! I thought. As soon as nobody was looking, I made a mad dash back over to Sophie's bed.

"What now?" she snapped, raising her head. "Can't an old girl get any peace?"

I stood my puggy ground. "Just come and play chase for five minutes," I pleaded, giving her the gooey eyes that clearly didn't work. "Purlease?"

She snorted and twisted her back to me. Hearing the noise, A Man Called James raced over.

"Come on, Bertie. Leave Grumpy Grandma be now, as we've asked you already," he said.

And that's how her name stuck.

*

Over the course of the first few months, Grumpy Grandma avoided me or batted me away like an irritating gnat every time we came to visit. Things only changed when the weather warmed up and we got to go on our first walk together. Good times!

Instead of telling me to get lost, she said, gruffly, "Get in line, Bertie Boy. I'll show you how to walk like a dog in my hood."

When she stood up, I appreciated how big she was – so much bigger than me. Sophie had a really bad leg caused by old bones, she said, which is why she walked with a waddle.

We walked over to Waggoners Wells, a place Anushka called Waggy Wells, a nearby nature reserve where I loved to chase birds. But this time Sophie kept me in line. As we strolled, I woofed away to her, only stopping when I realised she wasn't responding.

Then I heard her woof quietly, "Ahhh. Peace and quiet. Thank dog for that."

As we meandered along, I heard giggling behind me.

"Wassup?" I barked.

Anushka, A Man Called James and his mamma and dad were all laughing at us. Something about the way we looked as we walked together was funny, they said. The cheek! I wagged my curly tail and carried on trotting proudly beside Grumpy Grandma.

When we arrived at the nature reserve, Grumpy Grandma suddenly stopped and stooped down near a wide place of water. "Listen up, Bertie Boy," she growled, slowly. "I'll show you how to behave like a real dog. I'm taking a long slow drink from this lake and when I've finished, it's your go. Got it?"

I nodded. She placed her front paws carefully by the edge of the shore, pushed her head forward and rolled out her tongue to scoop water into her mouth at speed. I watched in awe. Once she'd finished, she smoothly lifted her head, looking refreshed, and shook a few drops from her face. I closed my eyes as the spray hit my face. But I didn't mind.

"I want a turn," I barked, hopping from paw to paw.

"Calm it!" she woofed. "Now do it just like I've done, nice and easy at the edge of the lake, okay?"

I rushed up to her, pushing my face into her face, to show how excited I was. She gave a low deep growl so loud that it vibrated the name tag around my neck. "Step back, kiddo," she roared.

I cowered, ears down. "Sorry," I whined.

"That's another lesson to learn, pronto," she huffed. "Real dogs don't rub their faces into everyone they meet. They sniff the situation out first. Didn't your dog mamma teach you anything a proper dog needs to know?"

"She taught me how to be a pug," I woofed indignantly, puffing out my ruff.

Grumpy Grandma snorted, sending spittle over me.

"And she taught me all about my Puggy Purpose," I said proudly.

"Ach, puggy wuggy nonsense," she spat. "Now c'mon here and drink. Just like I did. You must be thirsty, no?"

I slowly approached the lake, lowered my head, watching out of the corner of my eye to see if I was doing it correctly, and drank deeply. Behind me, I could hear Anushka nudging A Man Called James and his folks. They were sitting on the bench behind us, having a flask of coffee.

"Awwww, look!" Anushka whispered. "Sophie is teaching Bertie a new trick."

I breathed through the long refreshing gulps just like Grumpy Grandma had, and remembered to shake any drops from my chops afterwards. Then I glanced around and could see she was unable to help herself and smiled with pride.

"Not bad for a first-timer," she barked.

My chest puffed with pride all the way home, happy that Grumpy Grandma was my new best friend. I chatted about all my other friends and our cafe and my Puggy Purpose. There was so much to tell her, but a low rumble shook the ground beneath my feet and made me stop in my tracks.

"Ohhhh!" I looked at my trembling paws on the path. Was it a car? Or a plane? I looked up, but only saw Grumpy

Grandma's glowering face. She was growling at me so loudly, I thought there was an earthquake.

"Just shut the pug up!" she snapped.

I stared at her in shock but also with something else – complete admiration. "Grandma?" I asked, meekly, with my ears down. "Can you teach me how to make that scary growl noise?"

She shook her head and walked on in silence until we were almost home. Then, she turned to me as though she'd decided the moment was right. "Head down, just like this," she ordered, as I copied her. "Ears and eyes low. Stay focused and feel a deep dark rumble in your belly."

"Youwwww," I howled.

Grumpy Grandma's mouth broke into the first big smile I'd ever seen her make. "You've got a lot to practise, pug-squeak." She laughed, before waddling inside. "But keep on trying."

On the way home in the car, I snuggled down on the back seat and thought about how much I loved my new Grumpy Grandma. Underneath the surface, even the grumpiest person can be nice.

*

The next day, I woke up with two things on my mind. To get a Gravy Bone treat and have the biggest snoozle in the duvet that a pug has ever had. But when I settled down after lunch, Anushka had other ideas.

"I need to stretch my legs, Bertie," she said. "Come on, let's go for a wander."

I never need asking twice, so I stood up to wait for her to help me off the bed. I love my bed. I let Anushka and A Man Called James on it when it's dark, of course, but only if they don't take up the middle zone. The middle zone is The Best Zone Ever. Between their legs, I feel so warm and protected. Occasionally they move, but that's okay. They're allowed to. It just means I have to splay out my own legs wider.

Outside, I trotted beside Anushka, making sure she had her lead firmly in her hand. I stopped at all my usual trees, the usual scents of the Labrador down the road and the poodle across the way slightly diluted by the shower of sky water we'd had earlier.

As I stopped at my favourite-ever lamppost (it's several dogs' favourite in the area, no idea why – just plenty of pee makes it a good post!), my nose went wild.

Daisy and Lilly!

I pulled at Anushka's lead. "Come on!" I woofed. "I think they're in the park."

"Bertie, what's got into you?" Anushka laughed, struggling to keep up. "It's like you're talking me for a walk."

"You don't say," I barked.

Finally, we turned the corner and, yes, my snozzle was correct. Sherlock really had improved my scent. I woofed and raced over to the two sweet faces after Anushka had unclipped herself. The pair of them were wearing matching pink and blue coats. Daisy batted her eyelids at me as she always did, so I tried to be cool.

"Hey," I woofed, failing to be cool. "Found ya!"

We tore around our owners in circles. I sensed Anushka felt shy, but Kelly W waved her over.

"Lovely to see you!" Kelly said. "How are you doing?"

I focused on the girls while watching Anushka chatting away out of the corner of my eye. Bingo! Another friend for my human.

"Hey ladies," I said to Daisy, putting on my smartest pug woof. "See that? That's Puggy Purpose in action for you. Anushka and your human are friends now."

Daisy frowned. "Ah, you're so lucky," she said in her sweet breathy woof. "I've been wracking my pug head and still don't know what my purpose is."

I stared at her with sympathy, but Lilly was laughing. "Ah, don't worry, doll," she woofed to Daisy. "Your purpose is keeping me in line, okay?"

The pair of them raced around the grass so I joined them for The Best Afternoon Ever.

*

When we arrived home, Anushka told A Man Called James about meeting Kelly in the park.

"Sounds like there's quite a community building up through the pugs," said James.

I'm so happy when Anushka is happy that I barked, and they both laughed.

"Sometimes, I really think he understands what we're saying, you know," said Anushka. Don't I just!

They switched on the Silver Book. Anushka wanted to show James what Kelly had been telling her about in the park.

"They have an Instagram account for Daisy and Lilly, and it's doing really well," she said. "I had no idea Daisy won Britain's top pug model – look, there's even a picture of her with Simon Cowell."

We looked into the screen, and I could see a photo of Daisy looking awkwardly at the camera as a man held her. I sat between Anushka and James, panting as we looked at more photos of Daisy looking sweetly at the camera wearing sunglasses.

"Look, Daisy even won the 'Twirliest Tail Curl' at the Pugtown Carnival." A Man Called James laughed. "Brilliant."

"Lots of the pugs have their own Instagram accounts, you know," Anushka said. "Maybe we should set one up for Pug Cafe too?"

I jumped up and down, lolling out my tongue. I had no idea what this meant but it sounded like The Best Idea Ever.

CHAPTER 10

Anushka

The train rattled into Brighton station on the sunniest of days. As Anushka alighted, carrying Bertie in his rucksack on her back, she sensed him raise his snout to the air and take in a snuffle.

"Yes, it's so much fresher by the sea, isn't it?" she said. "You can almost taste it."

As they walked past the Marks & Spencer on the concourse, Anushka spotted Bertie's reflection in the window. He was lolling his tongue out with pleasure. A pianist was playing an upbeat version of "All My Loving" by the Beatles. Before they'd even crossed the station, Anushka was stopped several times by eager passers-by wanting to pet Bertie.

"Oh sorry, but may I?"

"He is so cute. Look! A pug in a backpack."

"Oh, he looks like he's smiling at me."

Anushka always paused whenever anyone wanted to fuss over Bertie. Spreading a bit of pug love was always a pleasure, not only for her but for Bertie too. She knew it didn't just look like Bertie was smiling, she knew he *was* smiling. People loved to ask what his name was and what breed he was, and often they ended the conversation with the same comment, "Oh, he's a handsome boy!"

Anushka felt as if she was carrying a mini-celebrity on her back as she slowly weaved past a crowd of tourists. She followed a map towards the main town centre. The manager of a cafe there had agreed to meet her, and she didn't want to be late.

Princes Cafe was another hip glass-fronted cafe with twice the capacity of Esquires Coffee. The manager, a busy-looking fella with cropped hair and a nose ring, shook her hand when they arrived.

Swallowing down a feeling of imposter syndrome, Anushka took Bertie and her notes out of her bag. This may only be the second Pug Cafe, but she wanted to come across as a professional. She sat Bertie on the chair next to her, and instinctively he sat with his regal pose.

In the end, it took around two hours to persuade the owner that he should allow a Pug Cafe event at his premises. Anushka promised to keep the dogs under control and clear up any mess, and also impressed the chef with her ideas for dog treats.

"Pugs have sensitive tums, so all ingredients have to be dog-friendly," she said to the chef when he joined them. "Strictly no things like chocolate or currants." The chef gave her a puzzled look. "Oh, they're poisonous to dogs," Anushka added. She pulled out a pad of dog treats she'd designed, and he nodded, promising to put something together.

Anushka also agreed to decorate the cafe herself.

"So this is basically a big party to celebrate pug dogs," the owner quipped, looking amused.

"Well, yes, you could call it that," Anushka said. By the end of the meeting, they had shaken hands and fixed a date. Clearly, this wasn't the kind of request the cafe had every day, but they were willing to run with it.

On the train home, Bertie sat on his human's lap so he could watch the houses and fields race by.

"This is going to be the best Pug Cafe ever," Anushka murmured, hoping she'd done the right thing. If she felt nervous about it, she'd tell herself it was nervous energy, and channel that into getting it right.

This was a new chapter, a new start. Who knew what could happen next?

On the way home, Cate, Doug's owner, messaged to ask if Anushka would like to go for a walk together in the park with the dogs the following day. Anushka felt her eyes well up as she held the phone to her chest. This was the first time in many years that a friend had asked her on a "friend date". The universe really was being kind that day.

*

Nicci's comment about her cafe being the world's first dog cafe had played on Anushka's mind, so she had a quick Google search while cuddling Bertie on the sofa that evening. There was one in Kyoto, Japan, claiming to be the world's first pug cafe, but it was a petting cafe where 12 dogs lived full time. They seemed very happy and lively dogs, but this wasn't a cafe run *for* dogs to enjoy.

She researched other cafes and couldn't find any specifically for dogs. Perhaps hers really *was* the first. Her excitement mounted at the idea of taking the cafe concept forward. Maybe they could run with it and do other themed nights, such as discos or cinema? Her mind began to fill with more and more ideas, so she grabbed a pad and pen to jot them down. While she doodled more dog treat ideas, a private message landed in her Facebook inbox. She did a double-take at first, as it was a vet who was getting in touch anonymously.

Bertie's next check-up appointment wasn't due for months, so this seemed strange. Besides, were vets sending out appointment reminders on Facebook now? Then she realised it wasn't from Bertie's vet. It was a different one. And they didn't want details about the Pug Cafe so they could attend it.

They didn't want her to run the Pug Cafe at all.

Dear Anushka,

We have spotted you are advertising for a new event called Pug Cafe. I wanted to get in touch to highlight how an event like this only serves to encourage pugs to be bred. As you might know, many pugs suffer disabilities due to inbreeding over the years. Many will live short lives of pain or longer lives needing endless operations. To encourage dog owners to continue buying this breed is an animal welfare rights issue, and I implore you to cancel future events. Pug breeding and ownership should not be encouraged.

A concerned vet

Anushka tried to swallow a lump that had formed in her throat. She was totally crestfallen. Oh God, what had she done? She had nothing but respect for vets, and anyone who cared about animal welfare was doing the right thing in her book. A long time ago, when she was little, she even dreamt of being a vet one day.

She thought about all the good press that Pug Cafe had enjoyed. Could this be a story that turned against them?

Bertie himself had survived a terrible side effect due to his breeding. Indeed, *was* it cruel to have bought a pug in the first place? And she knew all too well the issues with dodgy breeders. Look at what happened to poor Sherlock.

Her mind reeling, Anushka felt a deep sense of shame rising inside her. This was the last sort of attention she wished to attract. Perhaps this whole thing was a bad idea. What had been a wholly positive thing suddenly had a sinister slant to it.

But then again, pugs had been around for centuries – longer than many other popular western breeds of dogs – and not all of them had health issues. They came in all shapes and sizes, like Bruce. True, he was on a never-ending diet but he could run like the clappers if he spotted anything on wheels, Hannah had said. And look at the joy Doug brought to people. Anushka swore he was a Yoda in disguise.

Like other pedigree dog breeds, the issues they did have could be treated. Anushka always only recommended a reputable breeder and getting pet insurance if anyone asked her about buying a pug. They were dogs for serious owners willing to put in the time to care for them properly. She believed people should do their research to make sure a pug was the right dog for them and that they were the right owner.

Ethically, it felt as though they were doing nothing wrong, but Anushka also completely respected this vet's opinion. She glanced at the clock. There was no time to reply right now.

She was due to meet Cate and Doug in the park at 4pm. Her response to this unexpected message would have to wait.

*

Anushka put Bertie on his lead and set off for the park. On the way, her usual sense of anxiety about a social occasion came over her as she approached Cate and Doug. This meant making small talk for at least half an hour, she guessed. Hopefully, she wouldn't run out of things to say.

As they arrived, Bertie glanced up as if to say, "Let me off, please." So she reached down and unclipped him. Without hesitation, he rushed up to Doug, who took Bertie's enthusiastic "hello" in his stride. Anushka had never seen such a calm and collected dog.

Cate also smiled, asking her with genuine warmth, "How are you doing today?"

Cate really did have one of those voices that made everyone want to tell her everything. But Anushka stuck to social norms and replied in the way most people do.

"Fine, thanks!" she said.

Doug tilted his head, despite Bertie doing laps around him, as if he was listening too. Something about the way both Cate and Doug looked made her want to tell them everything. How often do we say we're "fine" when people ask us how we are? Often it's because we assume people don't want to know the truth when they ask. But Cate and Doug really did, and Cate's smile encouraged her.

"Oh, okay," Anushka admitted. "Actually, I'm not fine at all. I don't know what to do now, Cate. A vet wants me to abandon Pug Cafe. They believe holding pug events will encourage irresponsible breeders and more dogs will suffer."

Within a lap of the park, Anushka had blurted out the whole upset while Cate (and Doug!) listened intently. The last thing Anushka wanted to do was set up an event that upset people. She hadn't even considered this. All she'd done was try to find pug friends for Bertie. Now this had spiralled out of control. She pulled out her phone and showed Cate the abrupt message.

Cate nodded thoughtfully as she read it. "The vet's opinion sounds rather discriminatory," she said in her soft voice. "It shows remarkably little compassion for the animals already here."

"But then, we're pug fans, aren't we?" Anushka mused. "I suppose all vets have animal welfare at heart."

"Yes," said Cate. "But so many pedigree breeds have issues, and not all of them have illnesses. Doug is a perfect weight and has never needed any treatment because he's a pug."

"And there are so many pug crosses with fewer health issues but the same puggy personalities," Anushka replied.

They glanced down at Doug, who almost looked as if he was nodding sagely to Anushka. She reached down, unable to help herself, and gave him a good stroke. He closed his eyes as if he was savouring the moment. Bertie raced over for some loving too, not wanting to miss out.

"I think you should reconsider, Anushka," Cate went on. "Pugs are special little dogs who've been around for centuries. They bring so much joy to people's lives. You know Doug's been helping a little girl with learning disabilities overcome her fear of school this week?"

"Really?" Anushka said.

Cate told her the most extraordinary story. Doug had been visiting a special needs school where there was a little girl who arrived screaming every day. Her poor parents were absolutely distraught at having to leave her each morning. They'd tried to work out what was causing her terror, but no one could find any answers.

On Doug's visits, he was allowed to sit with the girl as she cried. Very gently, Cate said to the girl that if she didn't feel able to tell any adults what was wrong, perhaps she could tell Doug instead. The girl said something about "He was coming" and Cate feared it could be a safeguarding issue.

"Doug can listen to anything you have to say," Cate said.

The little girl then blurted out it was the wolf. Not only

from Little Red Riding Hood, but she bet it was the same wolf who terrorised The Three Little Pigs.

"Why don't we let Doug come with you to the library," Cate suggested. "Doug knows that these are just pretend stories, not real ones. That's why he's not scared. And he can show you he's not frightened of the books in the library if you go and sit together."

The girl agreed, and for the next hour she sat next to Doug in the library, even flicking through the books with pictures that had previously left her shaking with fear.

"That's amazing," Anushka said, stroking Doug's head. Anushka swore he made a brief zen-like smile. "What a gift he has."

"He can help people of all ages," Cate continued. "We make regular visits to dementia homes too. You know Doug doesn't judge anyone. He sits and listens and allows people to just be whoever they are. Even a person with dementia who may struggle to know who they are responds well, as they can sense Doug is a comfort."

"We all need more experiences like this, don't we?" Anushka said. "Not fewer."

Cate nodded. "I think the Pug Cafe is a special place where people feel they can safely bring their much-loved pets and feel truly welcome. The vet is perfectly entitled to her point of view, but there's another side to this story."

Chatting to Cate as they walked slowly around the park put Anushka's mind at rest and inspired her. Despite crazy busy lives, there seemed to be so few places where a dog owner could go and relax properly. Perhaps a spa or pub was one, but you couldn't take your dog there. She realised Pug Cafe could be a safe space where nobody was judged for having a dog, and hopefully where everyone could chill out – whoever they were and wherever they'd come from.

Later that evening, Anushka sent a polite reply to the vet thanking them for their point of view. Afterwards, she explained to James what had happened. He agreed it was the right thing to do.

"Hey, also," James suggested, "maybe we could eventually hold cafes for all kinds of dogs?"

Anushka hadn't thought of this. "Maybe one day." She laughed. "The Cockapoo Cafe has a certain ring to it."

CHAPTER 11

Anushka

Preparing for the first-ever Brighton Pug Cafe took months.

James kept trying to reassure Anushka that everything would work out, but her perfectionism meant that she didn't want to leave anything to chance. Triple-checking everything, she said, made her feel that things were less likely to go wrong.

Now she had trademarked Pug Cafe and set up an official business, Anushka felt under pressure to appear as professional and cool-headed as possible. This was becoming increasingly tricky, as the higher the event's profile, the more anxiety-inducing it became.

Days after Pug Cafe advertised tickets on social media, she had a call out of the blue from BBC Radio Sussex. Intrigued by the refreshingly different idea of a cafe for pugs, they were keen to interview the founder. Anushka answered the phone in a perfectly calm voice, but when they asked to interview her live on the radio, her insides turned to jelly.

"How lovely. I'm so flattered," she said politely to the radio producer. "Thank you for taking such an interest in us." *Oh my God, it's the BBC. THE BBC. They want what? Me? On the radio?* she wobbled inside. Somehow though, a calm and measured Anushka took over and continued the conversation. "You'd like an early-morning interview on the day of the cafe? Yes, I'm sure that's possible." *What are you saying? What are you agreeing to? Have you gone stark-raving mad? Agreeing to do an interview with the BBC, hours before the doors open?* "Yes, that's a bit tight time-wise, but my other half and father-in-law can help with the cafe set-up," she continued, cocking an eyebrow at James. "Okay, do email over the details to confirm, and I'll be there." *Stop. STOP! Argh, what's happened to you? You'll never be able to speak live on the RADIO!*

She thanked the producer and put the phone down. Then, she made an exaggerated strangulated noise that sent Bertie rushing over.

"Who was that?" James asked. He'd been feeding Bertie, and dinner was temporarily put on hold as they both looked intrigued.

"I've just agreed to do a live radio interview with the BBC in their Brighton studio," Anushka wailed, head in her hands, as Bertie pawed her feet. "Just before Pug Cafe opens."

Anushka loved listening to the radio, especially in the mornings when she got ready for work. BBC Radio 6 was one of her favourites. She always admired articulate members of the public if they were interviewed on the spot. Ad-libbing and cracking jokes was an impressive trait in people. Whether she could do the same was another matter.

"Awesome, Anushka, a plug on the radio will be incredible publicity," James said. "If you paid for an advert, it would cost a small fortune."

"Incredible, and incredibly scary," Anushka smiled wryly. She took a deep breath as Bertie offered up his ears for a stroke. She was way out of her comfort zone, but thankfully had her comfort blanket right there.

Anushka didn't have long to dwell on what she felt was a mad decision. Ticket sales were going through the roof. This Pug Cafe would be twice as big as the previous one. The pressure was on. So, setting her imposter syndrome aside again, Anushka threw herself into choosing fun props, sending recipes to the cafe chef and explaining how everything would work.

James watched with admiration every evening as she methodically ticked off her long checklist. Bertie tried to tell her the only thing she needed was him by her side, but she didn't listen.

*

When the day arrived, Anushka arranged for James and his dad to finish decorating the cafe while she stepped away to do the radio interview. She'd told them where to put the balloons and posters, and only hoped they'd follow her instructions.

Clutching Bertie, Anushka nervously waited for her slot in the reception of the BBC Radio Sussex building. Her tummy churned like a washing machine as she rehearsed a few lines in her head. She didn't plan to give Zoe Ball a run for her money any time soon, that was for certain. Bertie sat quietly on her lap, licking her face now and then. Like a sponge, he picked up on all her emotions and fidgeted on her lap as if they disturbed him too.

"I can do this," Anushka muttered into his fur. She took several deep breaths of Bertie's ruff, trying to steady her heart rate, when he suddenly made a flying leap off her lap. He paced mischievously around the rug in front of the reception chairs as if he was looking for a ball.

"What are you doing, Bertie?" Anushka whispered.

Bertie slyly scrunched up his brow at her, a face he often

pulled when he was weighing up the options of where to pee. He began looking longingly at a pot plant.

"Oh no… no," Anushka hissed, not wanting to alert the receptionist, who was thankfully on the phone. "Come here." She got up to grab him, but Bertie instantly took this as a sign of a new game. "Bertie," Anushka cried. "Stop it."

Instead of listening to her as he usually did, he took off for a game of cat-and-mouse chase around the foyer of the BBC. Each time Anushka almost managed to grasp him, he slipped away, lolling his tongue out with delight. For a solid pug, he could turn himself into a slippery bar of soap when he wanted to.

"You're usually such a good boy," Anushka chided him, giving the receptionist an apologetic smile when she glanced up at the commotion.

Despite herself, Anushka felt a rising giggle. Bertie clearly thought this was the best game ever. In a circle, they went around and around like a Tom and Jerry cartoon, until the receptionist cleared her throat loudly in a disapproving way. By then, Anushka had dissolved into laughter at the ridiculousness of Bertie's sudden decision to make the rug on the floor a playground.

"Sorry," Anushka said, as she finally managed to grab hold of him. "I don't know what's got into him." Breathing heavily, she went to sit down just as a producer poked his head around the door.

"You're on the air in two minutes," he said. "Follow me, please."

Without noticing it, Anushka's nerves had vanished, and Bertie lolled out his tongue with pleasure. His plan had worked!

*

Anushka arrived back at the cafe just before their first customers arrived. The radio interview had gone better than she'd ever imagined because adrenaline had unexpectedly taken over. The DJ was charm personified, putting her at ease, and had fallen in love with Bertie over the microphone. Anyone who loved Bertie became a friend in Anushka's eyes.

The eight minutes whizzed by, and they asked her to come back again if they had another Pug Cafe. Unable to believe she'd survived this far, Anushka enthusiastically agreed. But she barely had time to think as she rushed off to play host.

When she opened the cafe door, Anushka found James and his dad sitting on a table below a display of half-blown-up balloons stuck at strange angles. The bunting had fallen down behind them and a photo of Bertie was peeling off the wall.

Anushka remembered what a mess James had made of trying to decorate the Christmas tree, and wondered why she'd ever asked him. Creativity wasn't always his strong point.

"Everything's under control," James beamed. "As you can see."

Anushka tried not to laugh as she dashed around to redo the decorations. But it wasn't just the decorations she had to worry about.

Minutes later, she found herself looking at the dry carrot cake and shop-bought biscuits stacked haphazardly behind a glass counter. If Anushka had been a pug, she'd have felt decidedly underwhelmed. As if reading her mind, Bertie appeared next to her, cocking his eyebrow as he gazed up at the suspect treats.

"What's that, Mamma?" Anushka said, putting on her best puggy Bertie voice. "Are we doing a competition for The Worst Pug Treat today? Or is the chef just secretly a cat person?" Anushka laughed in her normal voice as if to reply. "I don't know, Bertie. Maybe, you and your friends will finish the cafe with a food fight?"

There was no time to make any new treats, so Anushka decided to make the best of what they had. But as she checked next for the puguccinos, Anushka realised they had no espresso paper cups, only human-sized corrugated ones, so they couldn't write the dogs' names on. After the attention to detail at the last Pug Cafe, this one looked slapdash and poorly managed.

While she was wondering what to do, James quietly told her something else. The trains to Brighton had been cancelled that day due to unexpected railworks. Most of the Pug Cafe regulars were now coming by car, but there were traffic jams.

"Oh no!" she cried. "This is a total disaster!"

Anushka realised how badly wrong everything was going, but it was time to open the Pug Cafe doors. She could see a big queue already snaking down the street, full of intrigued owners with eager and excitable pugs in their arms. There was no time to waste worrying about what was going wrong. She had to make this go right!

Desperate for everyone not to notice things awry, she rushed over to greet them all, handing them their puguccinos as they came in. Hopefully, if the pugs were happy then the owners would be too.

Quickly, the cafe filled up with smiling faces, all impressed with the décor. But Anushka spotted staff struggling to serve everyone in the queue, as they'd never reached maximum capacity like this so fast. To make up for the wait, she chatted to as many owners as possible and made a fuss of their pugs. If people had made such an effort to get there, she wanted to at least make them feel welcome.

*

When Anushka spotted the familiar faces of Kandeece with Sherlock, Kelly W with Daisy and Lilly, Arti with Gizmo and

Nicole with Barry, she couldn't wait to say hello. Despite all the traffic jams, they'd made it.

"This cafe looks amazing!" Nicole said. "Well done, Anushka."

Anushka tried not to groan and list everything going wrong, so she thanked her instead, and said she'd be back in a minute after spotting more balloons had fallen off the wall. On her way back, while finding extra seating for customers, she overheard a pug owner asking the chef if the treats contained only dog-friendly ingredients.

"Er, actually only the biscuits are dog-friendly, I've checked," Anushka said. "There was an issue with catering this time."

As hard as she tried to put on a brave face, she feared people would start complaining soon. Needing five minutes to gather herself, she dashed into the loos. Sitting on a loo seat lid, she stared at her phone, which had begun to ping like crazy.

I couldn't get any tickets.

Why can't you allow other breeds of dogs in?

My mum got a ticket but I didn't, so can't you just sell extra on the day? It's only one more person.

We've come all the way from London and it's ticket only. I had no idea.

Over 100 messages had flooded her inbox, and most of them were complaints.

Anushka had always prided herself on dealing with any issues head-on, but this was like whack-a-mole in the worst kind of way. She couldn't possibly keep up, and it was happening in real time. Overwhelmed, she put her head in her hands. She'd never felt more out of her depth. She should have stuck to her day job. Event management was best left to professionals, that was certain. She felt herself beginning to melt under the pressure when a pair of paws appeared under the toilet door.

"Woof!" Unmistakably, it was Bertie.

"Hello boy," she cried, fiddling to unlock the door. "You've come to find me, haven't you?"

Hearing someone else coming into the loo, Anushka quickly wiped underneath her eyes with a piece of loo roll to stop her mascara bleeding and then blew her nose. *Sort yourself out, Anushka*, she told her jelly-like self, squaring her shoulders. *You can do this. Even Bertie has come to tell you that.*

Then, a familiar soothing voice asked behind the main door, "Is everything okay in there? Mind if we come in?"

Anushka opened the loo door to find Cate, with her eyebrows knotted, holding Doug who looked equally concerned. "Anushka," she said. "I thought I saw you dash off. How are you doing?"

Anushka tried to pass off a watery smile as something genuine, but Cate took her hand and led her to a nearby side room where she sat down. Doug jumped up on the chair and squished himself next to her, feeling like a comforting hot water bottle. He gazed up at her, willing her to tell them everything.

"Seems I'm running a Calamity Cafe, not a Pug Cafe," Anushka confided in both of them. She reeled off the list of the disasters, as Doug stared with his liquid-brown eyes full of sympathy.

Very gently, Cate reeled off a list of several wonderful things she'd seen happen at the cafe so far. How Vicky had made it down with Henry and Percy. She hadn't travelled this far in years, and Pug Cafe had been a great incentive for her. How she'd overheard several people saying they'd never been to anything as wonderful for dogs as this. How people had asked several times where it was going to be held next.

"And have you any idea how many people find puguccinos hilariously funny?" She winked. "From the customer's viewpoint, nobody has noticed anything has gone wrong, honestly."

Anushka wiped her brow. This was news to her. "Ah, you must think I'm such an idiot for getting so stressed when it was something I organised myself." She gave a half-laugh.

"Not at all," said Cate. "And neither does Doug. Do you, Doug?" Right on cue, Doug pushed his velvety ears in Anushka's direction.

Anushka took a handful of ear. Cate was right about Doug. He was like a mini Buddha, sitting there absorbing all the upset. It was impossible not to feel calmer after she'd offloaded everything. *Whatever happens next,* she told herself, *just try to channel some of their inner calm for the last couple of hours of the cafe.*

"You and Doug give excellent pep talks," Anushka said, thanking them both.

As she re-joined the main cafe, a pretty petite woman approached her with two pugs at her feet. She walked with a sense of trepidation while her dogs walked calmly in front of her, as if making sure the path was clear. They reminded Anushka of a pair of bouncers ushering in their VIP guest.

"I'm Vicky," the woman said, offering her hand. "Henry and Percy's owner. I sent you the Facebook message a while ago about coming to the pug meet up."

Anushka remembered the strawberry blonde lady who stayed on the edge of the crowd in the park and her message afterwards. "Oh, it's so nice to finally meet you properly," Anushka said, pulling up a chair. She was sure lots of things needed sorting in the cafe, but decided that for the last few hours everything could wait. This was her chance to get to know people. "Henry and Percy look as if they look after you," she laughed.

Vicky giggled at them sitting like statues on either side of her, not moving a muscle except for their eyes swivelling around the room. "They do," she said. "In far more ways than you could ever imagine. Just after I bought Henry, I suddenly fell unwell with this rare neurological condition that makes my face and left-hand side go into a spasm. It took the doctors ages to find what was wrong, so I spent months in hospital."

Anushka had never heard of such a condition and, not for the first time, felt thankful for her own good health. "Who looked after Henry, then?" she asked.

"I did." Vicky smiled. "I confided in a nurse how important Henry is to me, so they let him into my hospital bed. He lay by my side the whole time. Like he was guarding not only me but my health too."

As Vicky spoke, Henry eyeballed Anushka with suspicion. She could tell how protective he was over Vicky, so she gave him a little stroke, which seemed to reassure him.

"As I recovered from all the treatments, I could barely leave my house for almost a year," Vicky went on. "But Henry was like a supportive cheerleader. Every step I took, he took with me." Henry stood to attention, hearing his name again, ready for action. "He was my focus," she said. "A reason to get out of bed every day and push on."

As Vicky's health improved, she got another pug, Percy. Percy was a softer character but equally protective. The initial pug meet up in the park was one of the first social events Vicky had attended for a whole year.

"I was worried people would judge the way I look, but nobody did," she smiled. "Henry and Percy had a ball too.

I've become friends with Kelly since then. Our dogs have even been out on a double date for a walk in the park since the first cafe. Did you know Henry and Daisy are so alike with their calm, gentle personalities, while Lilly and Percy go nuts around them?"

Anushka was delighted. Hearing how the cafe was bringing people together was such a tonic.

At that moment, another pug and their owner arrived. They were short of breath – they'd almost missed their time slot, and there was only 15 minutes to spare. The woman, a tall dark-haired lady, maybe in her early 50s, wore a pencil skirt and what Anushka recognised as a Chanel tweed jacket. Her faun pug was in her arms.

"Sorry I am so late," she said in a plummy voice. "Bloody trains."

Anushka stood up to offer her a puguccino. "And who do we have here?" she asked.

"Oh, this is Allegra Tiger Popsy," the lady said, in one breath. "And I am Catriona."

"Oooh, hello," said Anushka, sensing Vicky raise an eyebrow. "That's a lovely name." And, as she did for all the pugs, Anushka set about writing the name on the cup. "Here's your puguccino – welcome to Pug Cafe," she said, passing the cup over.

But Catriona didn't take it. "Erm, you've only written

'Allegra'," she said, prodding at the cup. "Her full name is Allegra Tiger Popsy. We don't do name shortenings."

Anushka laughed, as did Vicky, assuming Catriona was joking, but quickly they realised she wasn't. "Ah, sorry," Anushka said, cramming the words onto the cup around its entire circumference. "There you go. Wouldn't want Allegra Tiger Popsy to be confused."

The woman's face erupted into a huge smile. "It's wonderful to be surrounded by like-minded people," she said, gazing around the room. "This place is magical. I can release my inner pug lady here without shame."

Anushka beamed at her. "I'm so happy you like it."

By the end of the afternoon, a total of 700 people had walked through the doors. It had been frantic, fast-paced and chaotic. But somehow it had worked.

When she began tidying up, Anushka confessed to Kandeece and Kelly, behind the scenes, that nothing had gone to plan. But, like Cate had said, nobody had noticed.

"Well," Kelly said. "Nobody noticed any of the hiccups. Often people don't enjoy their own parties, do they?"

Anushka laughed. She'd never had a party before, so didn't know what it felt like, but perhaps Kelly was right.

*

That evening, the Pug Cafe Instagram account and Bertie's Facebook page were awash with photos and videos of the afternoon. Anushka loved to watch all of the smiling faces and excited pugs. Then, a new member popped up. Her name was Jade, and she posted a photo of a painting of a pug she'd done. It was brilliant. She wrote a message offering to paint anyone's pug for a small donation to charity.

"Wow, look at this," Anushka said to James.

He peered at the screen. "She's very talented," he said. "Has she attended Pug Cafe before?"

"I don't think so." Anushka frowned, scrolling through her page. She didn't have any photos of herself up. "And she doesn't seem to have a dog of her own either."

They agreed that whoever Jade was, she was clearly a huge pug fan, so Anushka sent her a quick message welcoming her to the group. Not for the first time, Anushka noticed that Pug Cafe extended beyond the doors of a building.

Buoyed by the success, already feeling so far out of her comfort zone, she wondered if she should go for it and arrange a cafe in what felt like the most ambitious place of all.

London.

CHAPTER 12

Bertie

I love being a pug. There's lots to love about it.

Not only do we look adorable, but wherever I go, a face like mine shines back at me. It's on a disc holding Anushka's keys. On a mug, from which she drinks that horrible black stuff. On her pyjamas she wears on my bed. And, of course, my face is kept on her phone and Silver Book, just so she can show other humans how adorable I am. And why wouldn't she?

So it was no surprise when Barry told us he was having a pool party for his fourth birthday. His human wanted to celebrate in style because, after all, it's what we deserve. I've had a couple of birthdays myself, one when I was only six months old. That's how awesome I am.

But Barry was having the biggest party I'd ever heard of, with a swimming pool too. Not that I knew what a swimming pool was, having never used one. So Barry and Gizmo filled me in at the last cafe.

"Think lilo floats, think sunshine, think humans going crazy with their cameras," drawled Barry. "You get the picture, Bertie?"

Actually I didn't, but woofed along because it sounded exciting, and if Barry liked it then it must be cool.

On the big day, A Man Called James seemed to find everything very amusing. "I can't believe they've hired the whole of The High House for an Ibiza party for a dog. It's a Georgian manor house!" he said. "I hope nobody pees anywhere they shouldn't."

Anushka dressed me up in a smart harness and bowtie for the occasion, and we set off in the car to a place called Fillongley. When we arrived, my snozzle went wild with scents of around 40 pugs, French bulldogs, chihuahuas and poodles.

So many faces came into view, I could hardly keep up. A Man Called James was impressed, I could tell, as he kept pointing out the barbecue and the dog treats galore. A man with a camera was roaming around taking pictures of pugs whenever he could. He didn't seem to think we were ugly!

It turned out that only the humans were allowed inside the house, but that didn't matter, not with so much fun going on outside. Naturally, that's where I found Barry and Gizmo, side by side, in matching shirts with flower garlands around their necks, giving their best gooey eyes to passing cameras.

"Dude, over here," yelled Barry, when he spotted me watching. He didn't often come over to greet anyone, so I felt honoured. "Welcome to my party, Bert. Follow me."

I trotted after him to find a huge expanse of water shimmering in the sunshine.

"This, my friend, is our pool for today. Enjoy," Barry said, daintily putting a paw in to test the temperature. Then he gracefully jumped in, creating enough of a splash to soak me.

"But pugs aren't supposed to like water," I barked. As I shook my fur again, Barry clambered onto a lilo in the shape of a flamingo.

"What's stopping you, dude?" he said, lying back, showing off his belly. "This kind of water is not the same as sky water in a muddy park, I assure you."

"Okay," I woofed nervously.

The water had a strong smell I wasn't sure of. But Barry looked relaxed enough as he floated to the edge before his human pulled him out. I tried to tell myself this was the same as a bath at home, as I tried to pluck up courage with Barry watching me.

"Cool, man," I barked, watching Nicole dry Barry with a towel. "Just gearing up."

"Dogs aren't usually allowed to go near a human's pool," Barry grinned, enjoying the rubdown. "But," he said, clattering his nails on the concrete on the side, "they are at *my* party."

Anushka came over, smiling. "How's it going, Nic? This party is pugtastic."

"We've sold so many raffle tickets," Nicole said, breathlessly, as she changed Barry into fake snakeskin leather minishorts and a vest covered in tiny palm trees. "All the profits are going to our local children's hospice in need. Catriona's been great at selling tickets. But my God, it's hard work organising something like this, isn't it? I don't know how you do it with the Pug Cafe."

One lady pug who I'd spotted at the Brighton cafe, but hadn't had a chance to woof to, dashed over. She wore a diamante collar and had such a glow about her that I was mesmerised. "Darling!" she woofed. "Allegra Tiger Popsy, but just call me Tigs for short."

She was a posh pug, if ever I'd heard one! We brushed noses and licked faces, and Tigs smelled like candy floss and perfume. She licked my head "hello", until her owner told her to stop.

"Ignore her," Tigs woofed. "She fears I'll go wild if I meet too many boy dogs." She winked, and I felt my fur stand on end.

"No worries on that score," I woofed.

"I've never seen so many pugs in one place," Tigs woofed, ignoring her human's request to return to a little handbag she carried her in. "Usually, all I have is a Siamese cat to keep me company."

I was horrified. "Sounds traumatic," I woofed. "Well, you're always welcome here."

At that moment, a mamma of two small humans tapped Nicole on the shoulder. It was her sister, Nicole told Anushka. "Nic, I brought my baby girl's swimming floats for them to use in the pool but look…" the lady said.

We spun around to see two pugs wearing sunglasses, both sitting in the children's floats. Another Frenchie was sitting in a lilo in the shape of a cassette tape next to them, having his photo taken. Nicole and Anushka couldn't help giggling, but I don't think the sister was impressed.

"Would you like a turn in the pool, Bertie?" asked Anushka. I lolled out my tongue to say "yes". Despite my doubts, I wanted to prove to Barry that I could do it. But it looked cold, and I didn't really know how to swim. Trying to channel Barry's bravery, I tapped my paws impatiently on the side of the pool while Anushka rummaged in her bag to pull out something I'd never seen before.

"Let's just pop this life jacket on first, Bertie," she said. "I know you're not a strong swimmer."

As she pulled a hard, uncomfortable ring around my ruff, I could hear Barry and Gizmo cackling behind me.

"Bertie, don't drown!" Barry woofed.

"Save me, save me!" Gizmo giggle-growled, rolling onto his back and waving his paws in the air. They both cracked up again.

I stood there with my ears lowered in humiliation. "Stop taking the pug," I barked at them.

Anushka and A Man Called James looked excited, not understanding any of this.

"Go for it," said A Man Called James. "Jump in."

Just as I thought nothing could get worse, a man with a camera came along.

"Go on, boy, in you go," coaxed Anushka. This felt like the obstacle course tunnel all over again, but there was no going back now. With Barry and Gizmo all eyes, I cautiously put a paw in, then shuddered.

"It's freezing," I barked.

But A Man Called James stupidly thought I needed help. "Come on, Bertie," he said. "You'll love it once you're in." He gently picked me up, leaned over the side and dunked me in. I felt like a biscuit in a lifejacket dipped in a cup of cold tea.

"Get. Me. Out," I whined, scrambling at the side. Anushka reached in and pulled me into her arms. I was sopping wet, with my tail between my legs. As she pulled off the life jacket, I could hear Barry and Gizmo rolling on the grassy bank with laughter.

I shook the water – and embarrassment – off myself as hard as I could.

"Come on, Bertie, let's forget about the pool and get some barbecue food in," soothed Anushka. I love my human. She's the best.

While sinking my teeth into a piece of charred chicken, a hush fell over everyone when a long black car pulled up. The driver jumped out and opened the back door for a groomed pug to jump neatly out.

"Oh my God, it's Puggy Smalls," gasped Anushka, dropping her chicken drumstick on her plate.

The coolest little pug I'd ever seen trotted around nodding at everyone, while we sat and watched him saunter up and down the side of the pool. He really was like a major Hollywood star in pug form. His owner joined him and shook hands with Nicole and then the cameras went wild. I had no idea who he was, but he was a Very Important Pug if I ever saw one.

A Man Called James whispered to Anushka that Puggy Smalls had a billion views on social media. Whatever this meant, it impressed the humans. I glanced over at Barry, whose face had turned into a bulldog chewing a wasp.

"Don't worry, Barry," I woofed. "I bet he can't swim as well as you can."

I'd just snuffled this sentence when Puggy Smalls suddenly ran to the edge of the pool. He paused, then seamlessly dived in. He doggy-paddled to the surface and snorted water from his snozzle, much to the delight of the owners applauding. He pawed water in one spot to give some gooey eyes for photos before paddling back to the edge of the pool. His owner effortlessly pulled him into a fluffy pug-sized towelling robe with an emblem of his face on the back.

I could only imagine the look on Barry's face, so didn't dare to look.

Luckily, right at that moment, it was birthday cake time. I'd already seen that Barry had two cakes. One had candles, and the other was a huge tower of dog food covered with cream that sent my snozzle wild.

The cake with the candles had a huge photo of Barry's smiling face on it, and when Nicole presented it to him, his lips curled upwards as if he was looking into a mirror.

"I bet your face tastes delicious too," Gizmo howled.

The cameras turned back to Barry to capture the moment as everyone sang and woofed "Happy Birthday" together. The party was back on track, and Barry was back in the frame. Nicole couldn't have looked prouder as we all raised three cheers.

"You're the best, Barry," I yapped. "Can you make sure there's some left for me?"

*

Despite the soaking in the pool, the rest of the party was a blur of cuddles, cake and camera lenses. I could hardly keep up. Puggy Smalls was a lovely dog, and we all had a good sniff and lick. He even impressed A Man Called James by barking out a rendition of Biggie Smalls' "Juicy" before heading off to another party.

Not until I'd met Barry, Gizmo, Daisy and Lilly, did I realise how much fun having your photo taken can be. While we sat by a verge near the pool, they explained how humans go gaga during modelling shoots so it's worth it for the treats alone.

"I'm the best pug, as I sit still," woofed Daisy. "Lilly copies me if she's in the mood."

Barry and Gizmo agreed modelling was The Best Job Ever. They gave me tips on giving the "pug eye", as they called it. Their photos had even appeared on billboards and inside shops. I overheard Nicole tell Anushka that Barry had appeared on adverts for LADBible, Now TV and Virgin Media, and his picture was on bags of food for Pets at Home. I'd no idea what most of it meant, but the bag of food was impressive.

"You wanna get your human onto this, Bertie dude," Barry woofed. "You get free food and the chance to be a pug who matters."

Barry's chest puffed with so much pride that I wondered if he would burst out of his harness underneath his vest. Apparently, it was handmade by humans, from tweed, he told me.

Anushka always made me feel like I mattered, but Barry said modelling meant human worship at a different level.

"Modelling sets you apart from the regular hounds," Gizmo added, flashing a set of white teeth. Both of them were regularly groomed for free too, as a perk of the job, they explained.

"More brushing, more attention, more treats," Barry went on. "What's not to love?"

My nose twitched. They smelled different too.

As if reading my mind, Barry told me he only accepted a bath with a certain brand of shampoo. "Otherwise, I just bark at the TV all night long when my humans try to watch it." He shrugged. "They know the drill."

Everyone knows pugs are cool, but this pair were in a different puggy league.

We were growing hot underneath the afternoon sunshine, so Barry and Gizmo muttered something about not liking to sweat and went to find shade under umbrellas made from grass.

As Daisy lay down near the pool, Lilly licked her tummy affectionately. I wondered if she would do it for me but I was too shy to ask. Daisy closed her eyes, but kept opening them again. Something was bothering her as she glanced over at her human, Kelly W, I could tell.

I looked over to check on Anushka, who was deep in conversation with all our humans. They were frowning. Nicole reached out and patted Kelly's arm in the way humans do when they're trying to reassure each other. If only they didn't mind licking each other as we do. But they don't. Humankind can be strange!

Anushka bit her lip and looked over at me, so I sat up and ran over to do a lap around them. That usually does the trick when it comes to cheering them up.

"The sun is out," I barked. "We have barbecued meat! What's up?" Anushka didn't even smile. "Hey?" I barked. But instead of picking me up for a cuddle, she carried on talking to Kelly.

I wandered back to Daisy and Lilly a bit deflated. "What are they talking about?" I asked. They looked at me with their sweet faces as if they didn't quite know what to woof.

Just then, Barry and Gizmo returned.

"Time for another dip in the pool," Gizmo woofed. "Who's coming?"

We chased him down there, with Lilly and Daisy joining

in as they flung themselves into the water. I ran up and down the side, only pausing at one end to catch my breath. On the other side of the pool, I could see Anushka put her arms around Kelly.

My nose twitched with the smell of human worry, but I had no idea what it was about.

CHAPTER 13

Bertie

A few days later, Anushka was talking about taking me to London, a place that Barry and Gizmo had told me all about. Gizmo explained how he'd been chased around a shop called Selfridges by a human telling him how beautiful he was. That sounded like The Best Day Ever to me.

I finished my dinner bowl, but instead of lying down to let my tum hang out for half an hour as usual, I barked by my humans' feet. "Are you gonna tell me what's happening or what?" I woofed. Sometimes, us pugs are the last to know.

"Bertie, you've got your first modelling job." Anushka grinned. "It's for a major advert – for a phone company. You're going to pretend to be a butterfly, or, as they call it, a puggerfly."

I cocked my head. I hadn't the puggiest what she was on about. Oh well… so I walked off to my bed.

"Ha, he's already playing the part of a diva." A Man Called James laughed. "Refusing to use his own bed again, I see."

Another unfunny joke, I thought, as I snuggled into the duvet. I closed my eyes and counted Donkey jumping over Gravy Bones, hoping it would trigger my favourite dream.

A few days later, Anushka put her lead in her hand, and we set off for the train station to London. I could tell something special was happening as I'd been spruced up the night before with a bath and had my nails done. Anushka felt nervous, I could tell, as she told me a few times she hoped I'd be a good boy.

I kept licking her hand. "When am I not?" I woofed.

We arrived in a posh cafe, but there were no other pugs. Boo! Only me. A man with a camera made a fuss over me. Or, should I say, he pretended to make a fuss over me. Us pugs smell a dog pretender a mile off. Usually, they stink of cats. Why anyone is a cat person is beyond me. Humans don't realise cats are the psychopaths of the pet world. Or worse, they do, but *still* think they're sweet.

I lolled out my tongue and gave him my best gooey eyes, making Anushka laugh, but the man didn't notice. He just looked at a sheet of paper and ticked a box.

"Okay, cool," he said. "I need to take a few still shots. The butterfly wings will be added later by the computer, so it's just, sorry, what's the dog's name again? Oh yeah, Bertie, on the stool please."

I gazed up at a high stool. Uh oh. I try to forget about my hind legs not working properly, but not when it comes to balancing in small places. I glanced up at Anushka, and she read my mind.

"Oh, er, Bertie isn't too confident sitting in small spaces..." she began.

The man shrugged. "It's what the photoshoot demands."

Looking uneasy, Anushka picked me up, but I scrabbled with my claws. "It's okay, Bertie," she soothed. "We'll sit you on that wider table." She set me down again on a more stable surface.

I sensed a few customers cocking their eyebrows, so I lolled out my tongue and focused on the circle of glass. Barry and Gizmo had given me tips on giving the pug-eye.

After a few shots, the man lobbed me dry biscuits. I gobbled them down, even if it was no Gravy Bone and there was no water bowl for afters. Thankfully, it was soon all over. My first job was done.

"Well done, Bertie," said Anushka, even though we both knew I wasn't a natural in front of the camera. I'd decided I'd leave it to superstars like Barry and Gizmo, after all.

On the way back, on the train, Anushka was distracted by her phone. I overheard that the next Pug Cafe was booked in London.

As we set off, I licked her hand. "I love you so much," I told her in time to the sounds of the train on the track.

*

Sometime later, we were back for our second visit to London, but this time by car with lots of boxes. I knew today was also a Big Day, partly because if we went to London something special usually happened, and partly because Anushka was quiet on the way there.

Last night, there had been more excitement over a newspaper. Once again, they wouldn't let me anywhere near it as they read out words with my name in it.

Anushka even rang her dad and told him. "There's a whole page on Pug Cafe in *The Daily Telegraph*," she said with amazement. I could tell she wanted him to be proud. She even mentioned tickets going in a private auction for £200 each for charity. I didn't know what this meant, but she was smiling when she put the phone down. This was going to be good for pugs!

On the way, Anushka's knuckles turned white as she clutched the steering wheel with a look of determination I'd never seen before. So I sat quietly next to her, panting at the window until it went foggy and she had to put it down. This meant I got to stick my tongue out of the car window. If you haven't tried it, it's The Best Feeling Ever.

We arrived at a cafe called Cafe Loco, and Anushka set about running around sorting out pictures of me and my friends, signs from the Underground station and balloons. I tried to keep up with her, but eventually grew bored, so sank down onto a sofa and eyed the biscuit treats.

Drooling, I waited patiently until I could wait no more and sneaked around the back until the person in the kitchen noticed my gooey eyes and lobbed me one.

"Bertie!" cried Anushka.

I moved away with crumbs around my mouth, feeling bad, but soon perked up when I spotted what was outside the long, glass window. Row upon row upon row of pug faces all gazed back at me.

"Hello! Hiya! Welcome!" I woofed, excitedly running up and down the massive glass window frame. "Come in, come in!" I pressed my nose to the glass and stared. I had more friends than I could ever imagine.

This, in a long list of best days ever, was *The* Best Day Ever.

"I love you!" I barked at my fans.

Anushka laughed, turning to look. "Not yet, Bertie. I won't be long… Where are you…? Oh my God. Just look at the size of the crowd!"

She dropped an empty box she'd been carrying to join me at the window. There were pugs and owners snaking all the way down the street, across the road and back up the street. Other people without dogs were holding up cameras and taking photos. I couldn't hear it – but I could sense a buzz of excitement in the air.

"Wow, what's happening here?"

"Oh my, it's a cafe just for pugs!"

"Let's join the line!"

Some of the people had strange accents, and all of them had cameras around their necks.

"James…" Anushka yelled out the back where A Man Called James was blowing up more balloons. "Come quick."

James came running through, and his mouth fell open. "It's like the Beatles have come to town."

Then, they both frowned and acted as if they'd drunk 10 cups of that black stuff. They seemed as excited as a pair of pugs!

"Okay, okay," said A Man Called James, clutching his hair while pacing around. "Let's stay calm. I'll stand at the door and greet everyone, and turn down people without tickets. We don't want to be overrun. You focus on welcoming everyone inside. Come on, we can do this!" Anushka had gone pale, so he gave her a hug. "What do we say? Nothing to lose, eh?" he said into her hair.

She took a deep breath.

"Yes!" I woofed.

I remained by Anushka's side as she finished off a few bits, to cheer her on. Then, it was time to open the doors for our new friends. While Anushka said hello to everyone, I ran back and forth, pushing my snozzle into as many beautiful crinkly pug faces and curly waggle tails as I could. So many sights and smells – glorious.

Only after an hour or so did I notice A Man Called James had beads of sweat on his forehead and Anushka hadn't stopped moving from the counter to the front. Nobody seemed to know how much money to swap for dog treats, so she had to explain everything to everyone.

I was so happy to see Doug, who, despite the crowd, calmly walked around as if he floated on air.

"Nice to see you, Bertie," he woofed, politely. "Quite a set-up you have here. Bravo."

It was so lovely to see Sherlock, Henry, Percy, Pearl, Bruce and, of course, Barry and Gizmo, who minced in wearing matching sparkling waistcoats. They headed straight for the high stools by the counter, of course. Tigs also turned up, and we chased each other up and down the panel of glass, as people outside pressed their noses and hands to the window.

"I feel like a pug movie star," woofed Tigs, as she posed for pictures with Pearl, giving their best head tilts.

This really was The Best Cafe Ever.

Many, many pugs and photos later, we said goodbye to the final wiggly tail disappearing out the door. Both Anushka and A Man Called James collapsed onto the sofa, then raised their palms and said, "High Five." They looked so exhausted that even I held off for a moment before asking for a cuddle.

"You need my bed," I woofed. I could tell they were happy.

We were all amazed by how many pugs had turned up. Anushka said 2,000 humans came too, and more pugs than I'd ever seen in my life.

Only then did I realise two very special pugs had been missing.

Daisy and Lilly.

They always came to every Pug Cafe. Where had they been? I whined on Anushka's lap to ask her, but she didn't understand.

"Yes, we're very proud of you too, Bertie," she said, kissing my head.

"Of course you are," I woofed, pleased. But, just like humans, I had a niggling worry now. Where were Daisy and Lilly? What had happened?

CHAPTER 14

Anushka

After the unexpected success of the London cafe, it took several days before Anushka had time to catch up with Instagram posts from other pugs.

Like most humans, she found herself easily losing hours while scrolling through funny and amusing social media posts. Between the pug meetings, all of the owners religiously updated their pugs' lives with cute pictures and latest news. Recently, Barry had reached 90K followers as Nicole managed to perfectly capture his personality in some hilarious posts.

The market in pet influencers had exploded in recent years, Anushka had read online. The most famous dog over in the States was another pug called Doug. He'd even reached the status of "celebrity dog", and Forbes named him as the second most influential pet in 2018. He had over 3.8 million followers on Instagram, his own line of merchandise for sale in Walmart and even his own trainers designed for humans.

The *most* influential, however, was a cat, also from the States, with an unusually grumpy expression thanks to an underbite. Grumpy Cat's following started off as a meme, which made her into a furry superstar. She had branded merchandise, including clothing, bedding, mugs and greetings cards, and earned a staggering $12m.

When Anushka told James all about this latest phenomenon, he couldn't stop laughing. "You'd think Grumpy Cat would be smiling like a Cheshire," he said. "Can we train Bertie to gurn or blow raspberries or something?"

Bertie looked up when he heard his name and made a low snorting sound as though it was the worst idea he'd ever heard.

"Think that's your answer, James," Anushka giggled.

While James went into the kitchen to get dinner ready, Anushka idly scrolled through all of her favourite pug accounts. She laughed at Barry's latest amusing post, which was advertising pet snacks, was impressed by Pearl's new designer dress, and spotted that Allegra Tiger Popsy also had a new account. Then, her heart flew to her mouth when her eyes landed on a post by Kelly W, Daisy and Lilly's mum, from days earlier.

So sadly I found a lump on my Daisy Doo. She has been to the vet for biopsies and will need an operation to remove the lump either way. Please keep your fingers crossed it's benign and nothing sinister.

Kelly had confided in the other owners at Barry's pool party that she'd found a lump on Daisy that needed investigating. Pugs can be prone to developing cancer, but usually only in old age. Daisy was only three and had been so healthy that she'd barely needed so much as a vet check-up before then.

Anushka guessed the results would be back by now, so she shakily reached for her phone to find Kelly's number.

The simple word "Hello" told her it wasn't good news. Kelly's voice sounded broken. "It's malignant," she half-whispered. "Daisy's got cancer and there's no cure."

Anushka moved the phone away from her lips to hide the sound of her inhale of breath. Then, she returned to the receiver to gently ask what had happened. She listened as Kelly explained how Daisy had to be taken to a specialist unit for tests. Tragically, she had the type of cancer, lymphoma, that recurred.

"Her only hope is to have chemo for dogs," Kelly said, between sobs. "It's about prolonging her life now. They can't save her."

Anushka thought of sweet Daisy running around the cafe,

carefree, with Lilly and Bertie. She was always so full of life and energy. It was unimaginable that all this time she was actually seriously unwell.

"I'm so sorry, Kelly," Anushka said, her stomach twisting into a ball of emotion. "This is every pug owner's worst nightmare."

She watched Bertie languidly yawn, stretch and shake himself awake from his snooze on the sofa. Sleepily, he waddled over to her chair to rest his chin on her knee. She longed to sweep him up for an immediate cuddle and hold him close. If anything like this happened to him, she didn't know what she'd do. Poor Kelly.

Kelly began to cry again. "Daisy is on my lap, now," she sobbed. "Totally unaware of what she faces. I can't imagine her not being by my side. How on earth will her sister cope too?" In a hushed voice, Kelly explained how Daisy would receive chemo in tiny doses, enough to save her life but not enough to make her feel unwell – thankfully. "She won't lose her hair or experience any of the other unpleasant side effects that human beings do," she explained. "Otherwise, we wouldn't put her through it all."

Anushka stroked Bertie's ears. She felt so helpless while she listened.

"The strange thing is," Kelly continued, "I noticed Lilly licking Daisy's tummy on several occasions. She started doing it more and more recently, so when I heard it might be cancer the vet hardly needed to tell me. Dogs can smell it, can't they? If only they could talk. We'd have had the diagnosis sooner. Then perhaps..." Kelly broke down again, racked with sobs of emotion. "Perhaps," she gulped, "we could have saved her."

"No, Kelly, you mustn't think like that," Anushka reassured her. "I know it's tempting, but there really is nothing you could do. Cancer can strike, literally, any of us – at any time. Scientists themselves say it's often down to luck. Cancer in dogs is always hard to treat. You're doing everything you can for your beloved Daisy, and I'm sure she knows it."

As Kelly sobbed quietly, Anushka swallowed down her own upset. The last thing she wanted was to cry down the phone too, as she wanted to be a support for her friend. Sensing the upset, Bertie moved from paw to paw, a signal he wanted to be picked up. Holding the phone between her shoulder and cheek, Anushka pulled him gently onto her lap.

"Has Lilly picked up on what's going on?" Anushka asked.

"She has," Kelly said. "Every time she licks Daisy, I sense a sadness. If she could lick away the cancer I know she would."

"You know everyone at Pug Cafe is here for you," Anushka said. "If there's anything at all we can do, we will." Kelly sounded so grateful, but Anushka felt her own words sounded hollow.

"We're going to be busy taking Daisy to and from the hospital for treatment now," Kelly continued. "So I've decided to use her Instagram account to keep everyone updated about how she's doing. I know so many people care… and… it means so much," she said, her voice cracking up again.

Unable to carry on, Kelly said she'd call back later and ended the call.

Anushka stared at her silent mobile, feeling empty. She held Bertie close. He went uncharacteristically still, clearly sensing something was wrong, so she gently reassured him that everything was okay.

"I'm just so sad," Anushka said into his ruff. "You pugs are like our children, you know? God, if anything happened to you!" She buried her nose into his fur, breathing in his slightly sweet scent.

Just then, James walked in with a steaming plate of pasta. "Blimey, has someone died?" he asked, sensing the emotional atmosphere.

Anushka's eyes welled up again, and this time she didn't stop them, as she told him about her phone call.

James's appetite disappeared while he listened. "All we can do is be there for them," he said quietly. "It's all anyone can say, isn't it?"

*

Everyone rallied around Kelly W and Daisy as much as possible, offering to help with the vet trips or drop off anything she needed. Like always, it warmed Anushka's heart to see such camaraderie, especially during such hard times. Pug Cafe was still a new business, but already the community of now hundreds on Facebook was tight-knit. Cate had recently invited other pug owners to join her during the next volunteer visit to the old people's home in the area, and the response had been huge. It was wonderful to think the wider community could benefit from the love of pug dogs.

But Anushka knew all too well that it was going to take a lot of work to make Pug Cafe a success. The love of pugs wasn't going to be enough to make it a viable business. A lot of the work involved in organising a business, such as sorting out tax and insurance, was jargon to her, so she signed up for a one-day course in a college to cover the basics.

During the lunch break on the course, when Anushka stepped outside into a courtyard, she found a message and link from Kelly P on her phone.

So sorry, Anushka, but I think you should see this.

Underneath the message was a company calling themselves Pug Salon, advertising for a pug cafe to be held in London the following weekend. At first, Anushka thought it was a joke. Surely, nobody had copied them – that would be ridiculous.

Yet when she looked closer, she realised the fonts were the same, and even some of the wording sounded the same as her own adverts. The company was advertising a pug cafe using the same funny logo James had produced. Pug Salon really was holding an event. She carried on reading and found there was a website and that the London Evening Standard had even run a story about it.

Hot on the tail of the Pop Up Pug Cafe earlier this month, it's time for more tails to wag because there's another restaurant for rovers on its way!

But instead of Pop Up Pug joint just for the day, canine café lovers will be thrilled to know Pug Salon is a permanent venue.

Open to pugs and pug fans everywhere, this one will not only feature the delicious Puguccinos, Barkscotti and Pugcakes, but it's going the whole pug, with all day AND evening events.

They will be serving Pugbrunch, Puglunch and even Pugtails in the evening. There are rumours a special Pug Disco will end the day's events. Held in the incredible Coliseum, the venue is twice the size of the previous Pop Up Pug Cafe event. So if you missed out on tickets last time, don't despair. This promises a bigger, even better, Pugatacular day out for all!

Anushka almost had to scrape her jaw off the floor as the words sank in. Then her phone rang. "Hi Dad," she said, trying to make her voice sound normal.

"I've gone for it," he said. "I've bought tickets to your latest event, Anushka. Can't wait!"

"What?" she replied, with another terrible feeling. She hadn't advertised the next Pug Cafe yet.

"Sorry we didn't make the last London one, but this one looks even bigger and better," he said. "It's a great marketing ploy to message people directly too. I had no idea my daughter was such a savvy business lady. Maybe you get it from your mother?"

"But, Dad, we haven't booked anything for our next Pug Cafe," Anushka interrupted.

They'd planned one for Birmingham the following month. When it came to deciding where Pug Cafe should go next, Anushka felt she could drop a pin in a map. But there was something about big cities that appealed to her. Every cafe so far had captured the attention of local media, and it only seemed fair to spread the pug happiness around the country. But the venues she'd approached so far hadn't yet given the okay, and it hadn't been advertised yet.

"Oh, but I had the invitation for this posh-sounding event in London and got tickets. 'Pug Salon', it's called. I wondered why you'd changed the name," he added. "But you know, it's got a quirky ring to it. I've heard tickets are almost sold out already. Well done!"

It was then that Anushka realised what was going on. Not

only was the rival cafe up and running, but it was even trying to cheat her own Pug Cafe customers into buying tickets. Even her own father had been sucked in.

She explained to him what had happened.

"What do you mean, it's not you?" he said. "It's even got puguccinos – that's what you came up with, right?"

For the rest of the training course, Anushka struggled to focus. One minute she was fuming, the next she felt like bursting into tears. After all her hard work, she couldn't believe someone could sweep in and do this. As soon as the course finished, she had a quick look at the advert that her dad had forwarded via email.

To her horror, Pug Salon wasn't just advertising a copycat event, they were even using words cut and pasted from the Pug Cafe Facebook page – and from her other adverts too. To add insult to injury, it was someone who'd clearly been to one of her events. They'd added in little details, such as the shape of the biscuits and writing names on the cups.

It was unbelievable to think that someone she'd welcomed into her cafe could do such a thing.

Anushka sat back in her chair.

She felt betrayed.

On the bus on the way home, Anushka tried to think of every owner who'd come along, everyone she'd got to know or hadn't had the chance to chat to. She tried to remember seeing anyone loitering around suspiciously, and she asked the same of James when she arrived home. He'd been manning the doors at each event, so saw everyone come and go.

Despite racking their brains, they simply couldn't imagine anyone doing this. Later, after explaining to James over dinner what had happened, he agreed with her – they had to find out who this was.

"Everyone has been so lovely," said James. "I mean, it's been impossible to speak to every single person and get to know them all, but I can't imagine who would do this."

Anushka logged on to the Pug Salon website to sniff out this unfair competition. What she saw made her even angrier. They didn't say who was running it and only gave a PO Box Number as an address. As if they knew they had something to hide.

"Who can it be?" she asked James.

James was updating Bertie's Instagram account. "I don't know," he said. "But leave it with me, as I have an idea of how we can find out."

CHAPTER 15

Bertie

Anushka checked and re-checked my harness until I wondered if she thought I was going to run away.

"I'd never do that," I woofed. "Where are we going?"

After a bath the night before, I was all spruced up. Was it another modelling job? I half-hoped not. I preferred to leave that to naturals such as Bruce and Gizmo.

Anushka whispered what a smart lovely boy I was. As if I'd forgotten! Then, she warned me to "be on your best behaviour" while we got on a bus and walked down a path with roses on either side towards a strange building. The flowers made me snuffle and sneeze.

"Bertie!" Anushka said.

The door opened, and a smiley lady wearing a blue-and-white patterned top showed us inside. The room had a flowery carpet, and my nose was bombarded with new smells, including boiled potatoes and… what was that? Mince! I lolled my tongue out, drooling a little so Anushka used a tissue to dab it.

"Welcome to Ivy House, care home for the elderly," the lady smiled.

"Hello, this is Bertie," Anushka said to the lady who was watching intently. "He's not usually this slobbery."

"Sometimes I am!" I woofed.

The lady looked at me with uncertainty. But before I could give her the gooey eyes, my friends ran up the corridor.

"Doug!"

"Barry!"

"Sherlock!"

"Pearl!"

"Bruce!"

"Daisy!"

"Lilly!"

We all strained at our harnesses as our humans pulled us back. There was to be no playing chase here, they said. We had to be good, they said. I wondered if the mince was being cooked for our reward.

The lady cleared her throat. "Our residents are going to come into the lounge, where they'll sit in a circle. This might stop anyone tripping over," she said, showing her teeth.

"Then the pugs can move clockwise around the circle so every resident meets every pug. Okay, everyone?"

"I smell cats," whispered Sherlock. "She's a cat person, not a dog person."

That was a bit harsh. She looked like such a lovely lady too. Often, I've found "cat people" are only ever cat lovers if they've never had a dog to love them. I gazed up at her with pity.

"Oooh, you do have lovely eyes, don't you?" the lady said, catching my gaze as if this was a surprise.

"Of course I do!" I barked, and Anushka told me to hush again.

We were taken into another room where lots of folks with white hair or no hair were sitting in a circle. I could smell something else – ah, toffees and mints. And what was that?

"Talcum powder," Sherlock woofed as if reading my mind. "With notes of lavender."

"Keep calm, everyone," woofed Doug, softly. "Remember, we're here to listen. Some of these elderly humans can't remember things, but that's okay."

"What does he mean?" whispered Bruce.

"I dunno," Sherlock shrugged. "As long as they have biscuits, who cares?"

Anushka kept her lead close while I wagged my tail. Then, a hand reached down to tickle my head so I looked up.

"This is Edith," said the cat lady. "She's going to be 99 this week. Aren't you, Edith?" The cat lady said the last bit so loudly that it hurt my pug lugs.

I could tell Edith heard it, but she ignored her. "What kind of dog, are you?" Edith asked, squinting at me.

"A super one!" I woofed.

Edith looked confused as Anushka explained about the pug breed and our ancestors in China. "You've come a long way, then," she said. "Better give you a biscuit, eh?"

Edith threw a delicious digestive my way. She was now my best friend there. But it was time to move on already, this time to a lady called Jane.

"It's a little pig," Jane said, peering at me over glasses like half-moons.

"No… dog!" I woofed.

"A pug, actually," Anushka laughed.

"A pug?" a man said. He had a loud voice, as if he couldn't hear himself. "What's that? A cat?"

"It's a pedigree dog," Cate said, gently, joining in.

"Never had them in my day!" shouted the man.

"I used to have lots of animals when I lived on a farm as a little girl," Jane said, quietly.

"What animals did you have?" Anushka asked, kindly. She's so nice to everyone, especially me.

Jane fell silent, so I patted her slipper gently with my

paw. It felt like my velvet ears. I wondered if she stroked her slippers?

"You need a dog," I woofed, softly.

"I don't remember what animals we had," she said, quietly, and began to cry. So I sat on her foot so she could stroke my ears the way Anushka does when she's upset. Poor Jane. She sobbed for a bit, but my ears soon made her feel better.

Just as we were about to meet our next person, Sherlock made a mad dash for the corridor. Someone had opened the door to push in a trolley full of tea cups.

"Oh no, sorry," Kandeece said, bolting after him. "He must be able to hear a fridge humming somewhere." We could all hear an echo of Sherlock barking "cheese!" as she chased him down the corridor.

I glanced around. Everyone seemed deep in conversation with their older person.

Jane was enjoying stroking my tail now. "You're a nice cat," she said. I scrunched up my face, which made her giggle.

My next new friend was called Dave, and he had the kindest face. At last, he was someone who knew what to do with dogs. He gently picked me up. "You got a gammy leg like mine," he said, ruffling my head with a good solid man-stroke. "Doesn't stop you, just like it doesn't stop me." I licked his hand in agreement. "I've not had any visitors this week," he said. "Now I've had two in one day."

"Who was your other one?" Anushka asked.

"My son," he said. "I love him, you know. But shhh, I'd never tell him that. We don't talk soft in our family. Things had been difficult since I left his mum when he was a young 'un. But now he's all grown up and loves his old dad. He makes me laugh every time he comes anyway."

I sensed Anushka listen more closely, so I curled up in his lap.

"Oh yes, you're a good boy, aren't you?" He laughed. "Well, let me tell you I wish human relationships were as easy. I might not have been in my boy's life much, but there wasn't a single day I didn't think about him. But everyone has their own memory, don't they? Not that mine is that sharp any more…"

Dave kept stroking me just the way I liked it. I yawned. So warm. So cosy. Hmmm… Gravy Bones dreams.

*

Anushka shook me awake. I'd dropped off in Dave's lap. I gave him a good licking, which made him laugh as we said goodbye.

"Have you forgotten something?" he said. I turned and spotted a Jammie Dodger sail through the air. I caught it perfectly between my teeth, and the chewy jam made my hair stand on end with pleasure.

I sensed Bruce notice it. He loved Jammie Dodgers. Like always, he was hanging out on his own away from the crowd. For such a big dog, Bruce always looked like he wanted to disappear.

A man holding something like a mini climbing frame walked in. I'd seen climbing frames in The Park – it's kind of cool to carry around your own little one, though, isn't it?

"Oooh, you're a big boy, aren't you?" the climbing-frame man said to Bruce, holding out his hand so the pug could sniff it. Bruce turned his back. Poor Bruce. There was nothing he loathed more than people calling him that. "Want a biscuit?" the old man asked. I could tell he wanted to make up for offending him.

"You can offend me too then," I woofed.

Six more sets of ears pricked up at the word "biscuit" as Bruce lolled out his tongue.

"Lucky bugger, eh?" The man grinned and held up what looked like a custard cream.

Bruce paced around in a circle, his gaze never leaving the biscuit. The man lowered it for a sniff. I almost put my paws over my eyes. Bruce was a gentle giant, but he didn't do teasing with dog treats. In one swift movement, he made a leap for it. But Bruce being Bruce missed completely, and crash-landed heavily into the trolley full of tea cups next to him.

Hannah raced over, her face red. But Bruce was already

upright, gobbling at the biscuit from the man, who found it very funny.

"So terribly sorry," Hannah said, picking up the broken pieces of china. "Bruce has a heart of gold, but he's clumsy."

"Accidents happen," the cat lady said in a sing-song voice that suggested she thought this wouldn't have happened if Bruce had been a cat.

As they cleared up the mess, we continued moving around the room in a circle. Now I knew that custard creams were in the room, it was harder to focus.

Doug sat on the lap of one of the residents, a woman called Judith. As a regular visitor to this home, this was part of Doug and Judith's routine.

Cuddling him made her nod off, the cat lady explained. "Some of our residents, if they're not with a partner or married, don't get cuddles very often," she whispered.

My next lady was Jean. Maybe she had a custard cream? I gave her my best gooey eyes, but she was more interested in Pearl, who was sitting next to me. "Is that a tutu you're wearing?" she asked her.

Pearl spun around, yapping. She loved nothing more than a chance to show off her outfits.

"Oh, I want one now," Jean said. She stood up and put her hands on her hips. "Do you think it would suit me?" She hitched up her skirt.

The other residents laughed.

Pearl was wearing a pearl necklace around her neck. Kelly took it off and handed it to Jean. "Her tutu might be a bit small, but you can wear this as a bracelet."

My last lady called me over. "I'm Doris," she said. "Are you as gorgeous as that last dog, Daisy?" Daisy turned when she heard her name being called.

Doris looked down at Daisy and gave her a wink. I could tell Daisy liked her a lot. Doris's voice was very husky and she smelled like something I hadn't sensed before. She smelled a bit like Daisy did. She reached into a bag and pulled out a bag of Gravy Bones.

"Oh, that's very kind," Anushka said. "Those are his favourite, how did you know?"

"I've been saving these for my favourite ones," Doris said, throwing us both treats. "And the one with the wobbly walk and Daisy will do."

Kelly turned around and noticed Daisy eating. "Oh, she's not shown so much interest in food in days," she said. "It's lovely to see."

Gratefully, I chomped on my treats. This was The Best Day Ever with The Best Lady Ever.

Then, cat lady walked over and stood next to Doris. She was holding a line of small round things. "Time for your tablets," she said.

"Oh, stuff and nonsense," Doris said, but the lady stood over her with a glass of water. She pulled a face while she swallowed them down. "They do make a fuss in here."

I could see cat lady speaking in a low voice to Anushka, who looked over in sympathy at Doris while she gave me the best chinny.

"Ah, she'll be telling her I'm not long for this world," Doris huffed. "Heart disease, it is. Terminal. They reckon I won't make it past Christmas. But we'll see about that, won't we?" She looked into my eyes and locked hers with mine. A lovely lady. I felt something pass between us, like I gave her some energy of some kind.

"Can I see you again?" I woofed.

She patted my head firmly. "We're friends now, aren't we?"

"Please do come to a Pug Cafe if you can make it," Anushka beamed, understanding me precisely for once. "We're having one at Halloween and another at Christmas."

All too soon, it was time to go home. The cat lady said we should say "Bye", so we howled. Everyone in the whole room smiled and looked happy.

On the way out, Anushka chatted to Kelly W and Cate. "We're so thrilled you and Daisy made it," she said to Kelly. "I wasn't expecting you."

"We're in-between chemo treatment," Kelly said. "Daisy

seemed full of beans today, so I thought, why not get out and do something different to take all our minds off it all?"

"It was really moving," Anushka said to Cate. "I wasn't expecting to laugh and cry in the same afternoon. The pugs loved it as much as the residents did."

"Wonderful, isn't it?" Cate agreed. "I always find these trips so rewarding."

"Especially when they involve custard creams and Jammie Dodgers," I snuffled.

Back home, Anushka told A Man Called James all about our adventure. "I met one resident who'd been estranged from his son," she said. "Bertie fell asleep in his lap as he chatted. For years, things were strained. He couldn't show his family any emotion. It was his upbringing, he'd said."

I snuffled in front of her.

"While Bertie slept, I went to the canteen to grab a coffee," Anushka continued. "There, by coincidence, I bumped into Dave's son. We got chatting and he shared the other side of the story. He told me how he'd learned to forgive his dad."

Anushka smiled, sadly. "'That's what I've learned since Dad developed memory problems,' Dave's son said to me. 'Every day you can create new nicer memories. Until slowly, they outweigh the bad.' So when Dave and his dad meet, they watch a fun film together, or dance around the room to a favourite track or he brings in some home-cooked food for his dad. And he knows his dad will love it. He and his dad hadn't ever laughed as much as they'd done since he was diagnosed. How lovely is that?"

A Man Called James swept his arms around Anushka for a snuggle, so I pawed him until he picked me up too. There was so much love coming out of all of us – this was turning into The Best Evening Ever!

*

Some time later, I found myself on a train to London again. This time, Anushka and A Man Called James were as spruced up as me.

"Where we going?" I barked.

A Man Called James double-checked the invitation. "Yep, it's the Ministry of Sound Private Members' Club," he said. "A party to celebrate Barry's official Blue Tick on Instagram." He chuckled to himself.

This was another party that A Man Called James seemed to find very funny from the moment we'd received the invitation. "I've never even had a party as big as this," he said. Anushka gave him a look. "Not that I'm saying Barry doesn't deserve it, of course," he added.

When we walked up to the building, I led my humans inside to find all of the gang waiting for me. "Yay!" I woofed, racing around Barry, Gizmo, Sherlock, Henry, Percy, Bruce and Miss Pearly.

"Come on in," Barry barked. He was proudly wearing a big, shiny, blue bow tie. Only then did I realise this was another party just for pugs.

"Is it Barry's birthday again, already?" I woofed to Sherlock.

He shook his head. "Barry's special but he isn't the Queen," he barked. "Nah, it's to celebrate him being famous."

"What does that mean?" I woofed.

"No idea." Sherlock laughed.

We trotted into the room. A man with headphones was spinning discs and waving his hands in the air.

"Good grief, there's even a proper DJ too," A Man Called James said. He picked up a leaflet and read it. "And all proceeds are going to rescue dogs in Thailand."

Anushka steered me towards a friendly-looking lady with a pair of scissors. "Oooh, Bertie, there's a dog groomer here too," she said. "You could do with a trim, couldn't you?"

I shivered as the lady told Anushka she also did shampoo and nails. Like any self-respecting pug, I like to look my best, but I'd rather sit next to a cat than a groomer in a dog chair.

Barry had fewer doubts. He'd been busy in front of a camera, but when he spotted me lurking by the groomer, he made a mad dash over to join us. "Hey, Bertie Boy, shall I show you how a pro like me does it?" he barked. He slid in front of me into the pug chair, while the lady whipped a napkin around his neck.

Barry's human Nicole spotted what was happening and came over. "Actually, Barry needs his nails doing," Nicole said. "As much as he likes massages and a haircut, I'm not sure he has time for one now."

"No problem," the lady said.

Barry's face dropped. The sight of nail clippers makes every dog's paws flinch. When he spotted I'd noticed his reluctance, he shrugged. "Take 'em down, baby," he barked, splaying the pads on his paws.

Unlike dogs, the only time humans stick out their tongues is when they're being rude or concentrating. I could see this lady's pink tongue appear as she took clippers to Barry's paw. He stared and smiled as she clipped… one, two, three…

"Yoooooooooooowl!" Barry let out the biggest screech of pain, making everyone stop and turn to look. Scrabbling in his chair, he slipped out of his napkin and limped away as fast as possible, leaving a trail of blood behind him.

"Barry!" I woofed, chasing him. "You okay?"

Gizmo glanced up and rushed to be by his best friend's side. But Barry disappeared, tail between his legs, around the back of the stand where the man called DJ was playing.

The lady with the nail clippers went white. "Crikey, I'm so sorry," she said to Nicole. "Barry moved suddenly, and I must have nipped his vein."

Today *wasn't* turning into the best day ever, after all. We all rallied around Barry as he nursed his hurt paw.

"My pawty is ruined," he woofed, licking the wound.

"No it's not," Bruce gruffed. "There's still plenty of food."

We all looked at Bruce as if to woof "shurrup". Sherlock licked around Barry's blood, gently making it stop.

"I'm sorry, guys," Barry snuffled. "I hate you all seeing me like this. Being a celebrity ain't always easy. However effortless I make it look." Gizmo looked as upset as his best friend did. He licked Barry's ear to comfort him, but Barry shrugged him off. "Sometimes it makes you wonder what it's all about," Barry continued. "I mean, cats don't get dressed up for a living, do they?"

"I reckon your Puggy Purpose is to bring joy into strangers' lives, you know, Barry," I said cheerfully, breaking the silence. "And Gizmo, when you two walk into the room, everyone lights up."

I saw a flicker of appreciation from Barry's curly tail.

"You think so?" he asked.

"Yeah!" I woofed, warming to my theme. "You're both insanely handsome, cool and funny."

"And stylish?" Gizmo added, glancing at Barry.

"That too!" I nodded. "Real one-off pugs who everyone loves! So clean up, get on the dance floor and we'll all bark you on."

Barry shook himself, ignoring the flecks of blood that splattered on the floor, and squared his shoulders. He nodded at Gizmo, who squared his shoulders at the same time as Barry. "Let's go," Barry said, walking off, leaving a trail of blood behind him.

*

As we followed, humans pointed and cooed at Barry and Gizmo.

Nicole came running over. "Oh no, you're still bleeding. Come here, my poor baby," she said, wrapping a tissue gently around Barry's paw. He looked down at his paw with annoyance. We all watched, not sure what to do.

"Do you know what a Bluc Tick is?" I asked Pearl. I knew she knew all about cameras and parties more than I did.

She nodded. "Hard to explain. But you know how humans love to look into their phones or laptops all the time?"

"Silver Books, you mean?" I woofed.

"Yes! Well, this is a set of pictures, and humans give thumbs up if they like them," she explained. "The more thumbs up they get, the more they smile."

That made sense to me. We all like to be liked, don't we? Although I'd rather have a cuddle than a thumbs up on a screen.

Nicole bandaged Barry's paw, and he seemed to be warming to the attention again. Then, when Nicole wasn't looking, her boyfriend Terry took a quick photo of Barry with his phone.

"We'll post this on your new Blue Tick account," he grinned. "Get a few votes of sympathy."

Barry pulled a face and stalked off, so we thought it was best to leave him.

An hour or so later, after joining our owners on the dance floor, Barry emerged from hiding again. This time, he was followed by Nicole, who looked incredibly cross.

"I can't believe it," she said. "Some idiot has posted a photo on our Instagram account of Barry with his hurt paw looking upset. It wasn't even a good shot of him and hardly got any likes at all, understandably."

"Oh no, who has access to the account?" Anushka asked.

"Only a few of us. But I know who it was," Nicole huffed. She turned to look at Terry who was dancing wildly on the dance floor, with Pearl and Tigs wiggling their tails around him.

None of this sounded good. I couldn't quite grasp what I needed to do, but then Gizmo looked at me in desperation.

"Bertie, we have to get a good photo together fast, or Terry will be in the doghouse," he barked.

I looked around helplessly. Posing wasn't my strong point, and I couldn't take photos either. But with Barry looking upset, we needed to save his party.

"What makes a good photo?" I barked.

"Humans love anything funny or downright silly," he replied.

Looking around the room with pugs on the dance floor, Sherlock crashing into the speakers and Bruce with his back to everyone, it looked like business as usual when it came to a pug event. But nothing especially silly or funny was happening. That's when I spied a huge cream cake on a trolley out of the corner of my eye.

I had an idea.

I went over to Bruce and whispered in his ear, then yelled for everyone to follow me. As if on cue, Bruce bounded over and sniffed at the cake. He then began licking the wheels. Just as I suspected, a human came over to push the trolley out of his way – and boom!

Bruce flung himself at the trolley. Cake and wheels are like pugnip!

"Let's go, pugs," I woofed loudly, as Pearl, Henry, Percy, Gizmo and, finally, Barry all dived in. Within seconds, cream and icing were flung in all directions as we lolled out our tongues with absolute delight. This really was The Best Moment Ever!

"Oh my God," Nicole screamed. "The pugs are having their own cake fight! Someone help me stop them!" Her mouth fell open as she waved her hands at us, but nobody noticed, because this was the best fun.

We started running around in a high-speed circle doing zoomies. Then, other humans began laughing and getting out their phones to take photos. So Nicole shrugged and did the same.

For several glorious minutes, pugs and cake combined together until I didn't know where cream began and our curly tails ended. At one point, Barry landed himself in the middle of it all, turning to pose for his human's camera.

Before we were allowed anywhere, we were all taken back to the groomers for a wash and brush up.

"It's lucky the dog groomers are here, Bertie." Anushka tutted, holding me at arm's length. "I thought you knew better than to do something like this. Naughty boy."

Half an hour later, we were all spruced up again.

Nicole came over. "Please don't tell the dogs off," she said, staring at her phone. "That picture of the pug cake fight I posted on Barry's Instagram account has skyrocketed our follower numbers. That photo was priceless. A shoot in a studio couldn't have captured anything as hilarious. I couldn't have set up anything better myself. Look, it got 2,000 likes within minutes."

With Nicole looking so pleased, Terry off the hook and Barry back to being top dog, everything had worked out. After a wash and brush up, he and Gizmo were back on the dance floor strutting their stuff, as if this was The Best Party Ever. Which of course it was!

CHAPTER 16

Bertie

As much as I love my own humans, sometimes I realise I'll never completely understand them. Have they any idea that having a snoozle whenever they fancy makes the world an even happier place? They can use my bed any time they like too. But weirdly, they only choose to slide under the covers after dark. What a waste.

They also have the power to get in the fridge any time they like. So why aren't they always in there? That would be the dream. But they only eat at the start and end of each day, and they even limit the amount they eat to human-sized plates. Weird!

Humans do things all the time that don't make them happy. For example, the more they look into the Silver Book, often the grumpier they are. "So put it down," I want to woof, "and look at me instead!" All of us pugs have discussed at one time or another how much happier our human could be if they were more pug-like. And we won't stop trying to teach them.

It's always fascinating to hear what everyone's Puggy Purpose is. Bruce told me all about his owner, Hannah. He was bought for her older daughter when she graduated, but Bruce stayed with Hannah after her daughter moved out. Soon afterwards, Hannah's man left the house, and Bruce became his human's new best friend. They walked for miles every day, The Best Walks Ever, Bruce said, while his human would talk non-stop to him.

"She doesn't need me to say anything," he snuffled. "Which is just as well, as I don't like speaking much." Hannah always came home happier, and Bruce was happy to have helped. "She calls me her counsellor, which makes her very pleased, even if I don't know what she's on about." He shrugged.

Although I'd helped Anushka make new friends, my next purpose was to remain by her side while she worked hard. I loved meeting new puggy faces and testing dog treats. Just in case they weren't nice, which they always were!

After a Pug Cafe was held in Birmingham, Anushka planned another one. But the next Pug Cafe was going to be back near our house, with Lovely Biscuit Lady, Nicci.

This time, Anushka and A Man Called James decorated the cafe with things I'd never seen before, including spiders, cobwebs and round giant oranges they called pumpkins.

The treats were a colour I'd never eaten before. They called them slime tray bake, rotten apple wuffins and eyeball cupcakes, which stared at me until I gobbled them up. Of course, the puguccinos were there too, this time in black cups.

Once I'd tried everything, it was time for the fun to begin. I was dressed in a wizard's outfit, Percy came as a tarantula and Sherlock came as a pumpkin. Then, three pugs I'd never seen before came in.

"Hello," I barked. "Welcome to the cafe."

They were three boy pugs, called Pugsley, Loki and Chester, known as The Pugs PLC. They were dressed in funky grey-coloured outfits – each one had a picture of a ghost with a red sign through it on the front. The pugs walked in together, and their owner put them onto the high stools near the cakes (lucky things!). They had backpacks on too, like the real ghostbusters. At that moment, Nicci reached around the side of the counter and flicked a switch on a machine to start a song. Then, every human began laughing and clapping before they sang at the top of their voices, "Ghostbusters!"

I ran around in circles. I didn't know the tune, but I liked it! People on the street stopped to stare into the window.

They took pictures on their phones as the owners clapped along.

"Der duh der duh der duh der duh du duh duh!" everyone sang, so I woofed too. The Pugs PLC were loving it, and so were we. When they'd finished their show, everyone clapped and laughter filled the air.

Bruce arrived a bit late, and his human, Hannah, apologised to everyone. "I'm afraid, as usual, Bruce refused to dress up," she laughed. "I did try."

"Never mind," said Anushka. "As long as you're here, that's the main thing."

Bruce said to me that he's not a toy – fair enough. He's a big boy and, come to think of it, most costumes wouldn't fit him. But he's shy too. Bruce always sits on the edge, observing, only speaking when spoken to. As long as he knows he's our friend still, that's all that matters.

I carried on saying "hello" to everyone.

Tigs turned up with her owner, Catriona. She was dressed in a strange beige and chequered top with a cobweb on her collar. "It's not my style," she sighed. "Too 'try hard'. My owner is a sucker for Burberry, though."

I licked her. "It's the pug inside the outfit that counts," I barked.

Then, Daisy and Lilly came in. We did our usual snuffle "hello", but I could smell something on Daisy that I couldn't put my paw on. She seemed thinner than her usual self too, despite bolting down a slime slice as soon as she arrived. When she was off saying "hello" to Sherlock, I had a quiet woof with Lilly.

"Daisy's not well," barked Lilly, looking distraught. "Our human finally knows now, but I've suspected as much for weeks."

"Oh, so that's what that scent is," I woofed sadly.

"Yep," whined Lilly, her ears turned downwards. I pushed my face into hers for a moment of puggy pause. She badly needed a pug hug.

"Daisy is being very brave," yapped Lilly. "She doesn't want to talk about it, so neither will I."

"Nor me!" I woofed. "Let's make everything really fun, so Daisy forgets about it all."

Lilly made a mad dash around a table leg. "Yesss!" she cried.

When Anushka is pleased, I'm pleased. And all afternoon, there'd been lots of human and pug smiles, with a good measure of music thrown in. Sherlock won best costume. I was asked for my regal pose enough times to make me feel even more special, and we all made sure all the dog treats had gone. Less for Nicci to tidy up!

Back home, the Silver Book came out, but this time they laughed and clapped. I sat next to A Man Called James and watched us all back in the Pug Cafe.

"The video of the Halloween Cafe has three million views." He grinned and squished my cheeks in the way I love, and then gave me The Best Chinny Ever.

"Bertie, you've gone viral again!" Anushka clapped.

I barked. That didn't sound great. I hoped this didn't mean another trip to see Colin The Vet. But A Man Called James seemed to think it was great too, so I wagged my wiggly tail as hard as I could.

CHAPTER 17

Anushka

The Halloween Pug Cafe proved to Anushka that despite Pug Salon choosing trendy locations in London, she could still rival them. Even though Pug Cafe couldn't afford to do "fancy", they could do fancy dress. She chose to return to their cosy roots of Esquires Coffee after the bigger cafes in Brighton, London and Birmingham.

The nurse from the old people's home called her a few days beforehand to say Doris was planning on coming along. The old lady had kept in touch with Anushka, even joining the Pug Cafe Facebook page to like posts. She'd also signed up to Instagram on her son's laptop so she could follow Daisy's progress.

"I had no idea that the darling dog was so unwell," she

told Anushka on the phone. "I want to come along and join her at the Halloween event, for sure."

But on the morning of the cafe, an upset nurse called. "Doris dressed herself as Magwitch," she explained. "She even coloured her face green with face paint. Oh, how we all laughed. But waiting for the taxi, she had a funny turn and had to go into hospital for a check-up."

"Please keep us updated," Anushka replied, with concern. "Send Doris a big pug hug from all of us."

Another guest Anushka longed to meet was Jade, the Pug Cafe's resident mysterious painter. By now, she had hand-painted hundreds of pug portraits, impressing everyone with her talents. Jade never took payment for her paintings, but she always asked for a donation of more paint, adding to her sense of mystery. Then, after the Halloween event, out of the blue, she emailed Anushka, offering to paint a portrait of Bertie.

Anushka sent a photo of him. A few weeks later, the most incredible piece of art arrived in the post. A beautiful portrait of Bertie, proudly wearing his harness, decorated in mini-pizza slices. Jade had clearly captured Bertie's cheeky personality as he beamed into the camera.

"I'm seriously impressed," Anushka said to James. "I'm going to frame it and put it above our mantelpiece."

Anushka sent a message to Jade to thank her, telling her what a great talent she was, and invited her to the next cafe.

Jade replied to thank her and asked after Bertie, but didn't say much more.

"She's Pug Cafe's version of Banksy," Anushka joked to James. "Quite brilliant, but nobody knows who she is." Anushka imagined Jade in a brightly lit studio working away with an easel, surrounded by portraits of pets, with pugs as her main muse.

Everything seemed to be ticking along nicely in Pug Cafe, with several small events happening across the country. But Pug Salon was still going strong. Anushka was intrigued, as James had been trying to unearth their infiltrator, but he refused to tell her how he was getting on. He said it would make her feel uneasy around friends, and this could ruin it, which was probably true. Anushka wouldn't have liked the pressure of any subterfuge.

As much as Anushka longed to forget about Pug Salon, the events continued to appear in the local and national press. Pug Salon held several events in high-end gastro pubs, serving puguccinos in real glasses with pug faces powered on top in cocoa.

One day, as Anushka was getting the Tube to go shopping in London for more pug props for her next cafe, she picked up a copy of the Evening Standard. Idly flicking through it, she came across a full-page advert for a Pug Salon Themed Movie-Star Night. Every pug was invited to dress up as their favourite movie star, and big prizes were promised. There were special rules for entry, including filling in a form to say who your pug was going to be, so theme tunes could be sourced beforehand.

As the train clattered through a tunnel, Anushka held the paper in her lap and closed her eyes. Not only was Pug Salon copying events, but they were even a few steps ahead. Then she thought of The Pugs PLC coming in with their Ghostbusters outfits, and Nicci's idea to play the theme tune. Had this given Pug Salon their idea? Was someone at her cafe the person behind Pug Salon?

There was only one thing for it. She'd have to attend a Pug Salon event herself to find out who was running it.

*

"You're not going in disguise, are you?" asked James, when he saw Anushka tying up her long dark hair into a bun. She pulled on a black beret that had been squirrelled away at the back of her wardrobe and she'd never worn.

"Whatever makes you think that?" she asked. She giggled, but it was really no laughing matter. Would she even be allowed in when they discovered it was her and Bertie, and not "Audrey Hapben" and "Boris", the names she'd given for her ticket? She'd bought Bertie a smart black tuxedo and a fake Martini dog-sized glass. Their entry to the competition was going to be James Bond. "We're off to catch the Bond villain," she said, as she kissed James goodbye.

Their ticket slot, also copied from Pug Cafe, was at 3pm, and Anushka didn't want to be late. On the way, she felt less light-hearted about what she was doing. What would happen when she got there? What if she wasn't allowed in? Would she have to confront the owner when she found out who it was?

They stepped off the train at Camden Town and wandered down the high street to a trendy bar off one of the side roads. Outside, someone was standing in the road with a huge brightly painted sign: *Pug Salon this way*. She followed the arrow to a staircase leading down to a basement.

This can't be it? she thought, peering down the stairwell. There were no other pug owners to be seen, and no queue either.

She picked up Bertie and carried him down the stairs to an uber-trendy cafe front. There wasn't anyone at the door to greet them, and nobody was checking any tickets. Was there even an event on?

She peered through the long glass door. It was clearly a trendy joint, and must have cost a bomb to hire. Inside, there were a few pugs running around a small dance floor, with flashing neon lights and a couple of owners chatting in the corner. She could only count five pugs. Several tables had been set up at the side with a few cakes, with several cake packets waiting to be opened. She squinted and could see they were packets from Mr Kipling. There were a few tatty posters of pug dogs. And, what was that? It was dark inside, but among the flashing lights she swore she could make out a couple of piles of doggy poo on the edge of the dance floor.

Dear me, she thought. *This doesn't look like a proper pug event. What was I worrying about?*

She strained her eyes though the door again to see if she could spot a manager running it, but all she could see was a man telling off a pug for cocking his leg near a table. Then, one owner grabbed their pug and walked towards the door, so Anushka swiftly stepped aside to let them out.

"I wouldn't bother going in," he said, looking annoyed. "Their last couple of events were pretty good but this one is rubbish."

"Do you know who's running it?" Anushka asked.

"No idea," he said. "I tried to complain earlier about the so-called dog treats, but was told just to write an email. I won't hold my breath getting my money back either. I went to all the trouble of dressing Sebastian up as the Sundance Kid for nothing."

Anushka looked at the little pug he was holding, wearing a lopsided cowboy hat with a red necktie. The pug's Disney eyes flashed with disappointment. "Sorry, Sebastian," Anushka said, sadly.

The man stalked off and disappeared into the throng of the Camden crowd with his four-legged cowboy. Anushka decided to join them. She'd seen enough. It remained a mystery who was running the cafe, but perhaps they weren't such big competition after all.

*

Some time afterwards, James stood behind Anushka while she gazed at her reflection in the mirror one last time. "You look beautiful in that dress," he said.

"You sure?" She sighed. "I don't know about the colour." She'd picked a dress with ditsy blue flowers on, but was never sure of herself when it came to dress codes. She found it easier to pick an outfit for Bertie than for herself.

Today was Sarah's wedding, one of James's old friends from university. Sarah had been with her boyfriend Mark for the past decade, and James had known them for what seemed like forever. They'd finally decided to tie the knot, the first couple in James's friendship group to do so. Dogs were invited too, so Anushka put on Bertie's smartest harness and he joined them – it was the least she could do for Sarah.

Hours later, they were sitting on pews waiting at the back of the church for the bride to enter. Bertie stood on Anushka's lap in his regal pose, ears alert to the sounds of the organ. A noise that clearly intrigued him.

"Bertie's first wedding," she whispered to James. "He's excited, look."

James slid his hand into Anushka's. "Hopefully won't be his last." He winked.

She gave a watery smile. She loved James, he knew that, but marriage was way off the cards. After watching her parents' marriage crumble, she didn't believe in being a bride herself. Besides, they were very happy as they were, so what was the point? And with Bertie in the mix, they already felt very much like a family. She kissed James's cheek and commented on the decorative flowers to change the subject.

A hush descended over the guests as the organ volume cranked up a touch to play the traditional "Here comes the bride" tune. Despite Anushka's own thoughts on marriage, she found herself welling up as she watched Sarah walk slowly down the aisle, resplendent in a beautiful white wedding dress. Bertie lolled his tongue out, equally impressed.

After the ceremony, they were ushered into a nearby church hall. Anushka clutched Bertie's lead a little tighter. All the guests were standing in circles, deep in conversation.

She felt heat rising from her neck to her face, as they all seemed to know each other.

Just then, her mobile buzzed with an unrecognised number. Grateful for an excuse to go and compose herself, she handed Bertie's lead to James so she could take the call outside.

It was a journalist from *The London Post.* He wanted a quote for an article they were writing about dog cafes. He explained that he'd already had several quotes from the couple who ran Pug Salon.

Anushka could feel her heckles rise, just like Bertie's, and she stammered as she tried to speak. "You need something today? Er, right now?" They'd caught her off guard, and she didn't have time anyway. She'd just heard someone bang a spoon on the side of glass inside the hall, indicating that speeches were about to begin.

"Yes. We're going to press in two days," he said, quickly. "I just have a few questions."

What Anushka really wanted to ask was the names of the people running Pug Salon, but she wondered if it would be a strange question. She had no idea what the journalist was going to say about dog cafes, so she had to provide thoughtful answers on behalf of Pug Cafe instead.

"What angle are you aiming for?" Anushka asked.

"We've also chatted to a couple of vets for comment too," he said, ignoring her direct question.

An alarm started ringing inside Anushka's head. "Look, this is bad timing," she said, politely, as James stuck his head around the corner of the door to see where she was. "I'm actually at a wedding right now. Can you email over the questions and I'll reply this evening?"

The journalist sounded put out. "Ah okay, I suppose so," he said, reluctantly.

Anushka put the phone down with a deep sense of dread. *The London Post* had a huge national readership. It was a liberal paper on the face of it, but from his line of questioning Anushka could guess the angle they wanted. And it wasn't a positive one.

After the speeches, a text arrived from the journalist. *Just a question I forgot to email*, he wrote. *What's a puguccino made from?*

Puguccinos are made from cream, something dogs aren't supposed to eat regularly, because lactose doesn't always agree with their digestive systems. But it was a fun drink that Anushka had designed purely as a treat. A bit like a McDonald's for humans.

She pinched the top of her brow with her finger and thumb. She knew exactly where this was heading, but still answered honestly with a quick reply. Pug Cafe had nothing to hide and was doing nothing wrong. She promised she'd answer the rest of his questions as soon as she returned to her laptop that evening.

*

A couple of days later, the article was published in *The London Post.* When James brought a copy home, Bertie licked his lips as usual, and Anushka longed just to give it straight to him. *He'll make light work of it,* she thought.

"I can hardly bear to look at it," she groaned.

James looked pale. He'd clearly already had a quick read on the way back from the newsagents, so she knew it wasn't good. In fact, it was even worse than she'd imagined.

The headline read, *Mine's a puguccino: pug-themed cafes and events are "irresponsible", say vets.*

As Anushka feared, it was a hatchet job. The piece attacked the breeding of pugs and, by default, pug cafes too. Vets were quoted as saying many pugs suffer from permanent disabilities and are prone to many health conditions.

The piece read, *Now vets say they are worried that the recent craze for pug-themed social events from pop-up cafes offering puguccinos – shots of cream in an espresso cup for the dogs – to venues serving pugtails for the dog owners, could make matters worse.*

"Take it away from here, James," Anushka said, tears smarting in her eyes.

Trying to reassure her, James said he'd already read the article and her answers all came across as sensible and honest. "Anushka, they included your quote: 'We encourage anyone thinking of getting a dog to research the breed, not just pugs, very carefully, take out comprehensive pet insurance and, where possible, to adopt rather than shop,'" he read. "See? You come across as the responsible dog owner you are."

Bless James. Anushka knew he was trying to make her feel better, but it wasn't working. She had no idea what the backlash would be. But one thing was for sure – there would be one.

Later that evening, someone messaged Anushka to say they had seen the pug story discussed during the newspaper review on *Sky News*. It had reached such a vast audience. Pugs were suddenly a talking point everywhere, and not in a good way.

*

Despite Pug Salon's event not quite living up to expectations, it remained a thorn in the side of Pug Cafe. Confused or angry Pug Salon customers kept contacting Anushka via Pug Cafe, assuming she ran these multiple events. Without a doubt, it was tarnishing their name, but she was powerless to stop it.

In a bid to stop worrying about a business she had no control over, Anushka put all her energy into organising the next event.

Pug Cafe's first Christmas.

She didn't just want to make it special for all their pugs and owners, but for Daisy too. Nobody knew if this was going to be her last Christmas, so Anushka was determined to make it a joyful event, with lots of happy memories.

Kelly W had been keeping everyone up to date about Daisy's progress on her Instagram page. She'd been so inundated with good wishes and presents that she'd decided to give Daisy one gift per day rather than an advent calendar. Mainly, they were gifts from Daisy's friends wanting to wish her well, such as a new bandana, tasty treats or a bed. Doris even crocheted her a small cardigan after recovering from her hospital stay.

A ladylike trooper, Daisy took all the visits to the vets in her stride. In fact, she was such an unusually sweet little dog that the vets didn't keep her in a cage like other furry patients. While they did their paperwork, Daisy was allowed to sit on their laps for cuddles. This didn't surprise Anushka. Pugs were popular, but Daisy was also a special little dog.

Following each treatment, Daisy always went home. She was still lively and able to go for short walks, but inevitably her illness began taking its toll.

Anushka had heard how tough things had been for Kelly too. The chemotherapy was so expensive, they'd already reached the limit on the pet insurance. Kelly and her husband were having to find thousands of pounds to keep it going and keep Daisy alive. Kelly confided in Anushka that she would do whatever it took to give Daisy the best last few months.

"We'll use credit cards or remortgage the house," she confided in her. "I'll even sell our home if it means we help Daisy to live longer and enjoy a decent standard of living."

Anushka really hoped it wouldn't come to that. Kelly had a busy job as a beauty therapist, but finding thousands of extra pounds would be impossible.

Then, the amazing news emerged that one of the other pug owners, Ellie, had stepped in to organise a whip-round. Everyone had been desperate to help, and now they knew exactly what to do. Very quickly, over £2,000 in cash was raised within days to go towards the spiralling £12,000 bill.

While plans for the Christmas Cafe were coming together, Anushka forgot all about her rival. Well, almost. Her lawyer got in touch, after monitoring the Pug Salon website. She advised that the only thing they could do next to stop the copycat cafe was take the business owners to court.

"That sounds very… serious," Anushka gulped.

"It's the only way forward," the lawyer explained. "If the letters are ignored and this carries on, it's a clear breach of copyright. You have a good case."

Anushka said she'd mull it over. Once again, she tried to find some information about who was behind the operation.

And once again, she drew a blank. James assured her that his detective work was still in hand, but they would have to be patient.

Before the main Christmas event, Anushka organised two smaller cafes to run in Cardiff and Southampton. The planning was still immense, but she stuck to cosy venues and limited tickets. She wanted to keep things fun and manageable, rather than try to build an empire. Each cafe was very popular and attracted new and old faces. It took hours to plan, and her nerves didn't diminish beforehand, but the look on the owners' and their dogs' faces always made it worthwhile.

Then, someone told her about another event in Cardiff, a week after Pug Cafe's. And, incredibly, the same thing happened in Southampton.

Shocked, Anushka looked up this second rival to see yet another copycat had sprung up, Pugz R Us. This time, it was organised by a guy called Derek, who appeared to be a Delboy chancer character running other failing businesses as well.

"I can't believe this has happened again," Anushka wailed to James. "I guess it really is only a matter of time before someone with more money than us comes along and sweeps us away."

James agreed that it was a risky business to continue. The fact was, they weren't wealthy, and Anushka had given up her job to make a go of this. Thankfully, this other cafe vanished as quickly as it had appeared.

Anushka knew running a cafe for dogs wasn't for the faint-hearted and, once again, was proven right.

CHAPTER 18

Anushka

The hunt was on for the perfect venue for the Christmas Pug Cafe. Since the last cafe in London had been a success, Anushka wanted to find somewhere central again. But all the venues she approached turned down her idea.

When she gently pressed one owner why, she was shocked by his reaction.

"After reading the *London Post* article, we don't want to associate ourselves with any Pug Cafes or dog cafes," he snapped. "They're cruel."

Anushka swallowed hard, forced herself to thank him and put the phone down. This was tricky. What if every cafe in London said "no"? What if Pug Cafes now had such a bad name that it was over? Not willing to give up, though, she carried on asking modest-sized cafes within their budget until she found a small cafe, Central Street Cafe, near Old Street in London. It was part of a local community centre, and all cafe profits went to a local charity. When Anushka suggested holding a Pug Cafe to the dog-loving owner, they couldn't have been happier to accommodate her.

Anushka could have licked their faces herself! But luckily, Bertie would do that for her.

With the venue booked, Anushka's thoughts turned to making the event as festive as possible. She bought a wooden sleigh from Etsy and spent a weekend painting it. Then she splashed out on a mini-Santa, ignoring James when he said it looked super-creepy.

Her favourite place for props was Poundland, and she would scour the shelves for the one gem of an item. By now, they also had lots of lovely pug artwork, including from their Facebook regular, Jade.

Next, Anushka worked with a professional doggy treat baker to make the festive fare. There were Christmas puddings, cakes, biscuits, gingerbread pugs and, of course, festive pugcakes and the regular puguccino.

While she kept herself busy, trying to think of more ways to make things festive, naturally her thoughts turned to her own plans for Christmas. It had been a busy year for all of them, with only rare moments to catch up. Lakmini now worked full time and had two daughters, and both of her parents also worked and had busy social lives. Catch-ups were all too short.

Anushka didn't know what they'd make of Pug Cafe or what she was doing. She'd only spoken to her dad briefly about them. He'd always been very supportive, but knew little about the stresses and strains. The Fernandos weren't a family to divulge too many details. But Anushka couldn't help but sometimes feel as if she longed to confide in them about all the ups and downs.

Then, out of the blue, her mum rang to say she wanted to come to the Christmas Pug Cafe. This surprised and pleased Anushka in equal measure. Her mum had always tried her best to make things festive, though she'd never mastered how to roast potatoes. She used to make turkey with fried rice.

Her parents embraced lots of other parts of British life, and the girls always had presents and a tree, but something always lacked when it came to celebrations. One year, *National Lampoon's Christmas Vacation* was playing in the background as they ate a silent dinner. Anushka couldn't help but notice the stark contrast between the laughing family around a turkey with all the trimmings on TV, and their own.

Frazzle was the only one who livened up events. They loved making a fuss of him, carefully putting his own doggie roast dinner together for him to gobble up. He lightened the mood, giving them a focus and someone to laugh at. After Frazzle died, Anushka felt even less like celebrating. Christmas was no longer a day to look forward to and enjoy. It was a day on the calendar to tick off like any other.

In recent years, her mum had converted to Catholicism and was now a regular churchgoer. Anushka was so happy that her mum had found her own sense of belonging and contentment. She had many friends and placed much importance on community and helping others.

Happily, her mum and dad had also bonded hugely over their love of their grandchildren when they came along. The power of grandchildren had brought this once-warring couple closer than they'd ever been. They really doted on them and there was nothing they wouldn't do for them. The children became the centre of their attention, and their hearts. It was so heart-warming to see, the way they played with them, looked after them and helped out even with school runs! It made Anushka smile to see her parents so happy in their new roles.

Anushka adored her beautiful nieces too. They were the centre of the family, especially at Christmas. They always met at Lakmini's house at some point over the festive season. They loved coming together to celebrate Christmas – it felt as if the family unit was complete once again. It was a happy time. But there was still a lingering part of Anushka that felt like an outsider. She was the quiet, awkward little sister who'd struggled for years to be honest about what was happening in her life. The black sheep who kept herself to herself. Now she'd set up this unusual business, she didn't know what her family really thought. Her dad often mentioned how much fun it looked online and liked to leave comments on the Facebook page. However, Anushka pushed these thoughts to the back of her mind. She was beginning to like Christmas again. Her mum, dad and sister all loved to spoil Bertie at Christmas too – calling him their Grandpug.

As much as Anushka was flattered her mum was interested in coming to the Pug Cafe, she hoped nothing went wrong. Her mother wouldn't know anyone there except for her and James. But, pushing aside any reservations, she replied to her mother's text message with a warm welcome.

*

Much to Anushka's delight, gentle flakes of snow floated down onto the windows as she finished off the last decorations for the Christmas Pug Cafe.

"I'm dreaming of a white Pug Cafe…" James crooned in his best tenor voice while he helped to fix one end of the paper chain to the ceiling.

Anushka stepped down from the ladder to admire their work. Wreaths with pug faces hung from the doors, and paper-mâché snow dogs were stuck on the windows. Tables were decorated with crackers with Bertie's face on them, and a whole buffet of Christmassy dog treats waited on the side. The scent of cinnamon and spices filled the air from the mulled wine, while jolly Christmas songs sang out from a carefully selected playlist chosen the night before. The dog sleigh was waiting for its first dog rider, complete with a stuffed reindeer, and the automated Santa was ready to wink and wave at pugs and their owners as they walked in.

With everything finally set, Anushka picked up Bertie for a cuddle while they waited for the first customers to arrive. "Let's forget all about Pug Salon for today, at least," she said to him. "Today is a special one for Daisy."

Anushka was glad they'd chosen a smaller, cosier event. This was very different to the hipster district of Shoreditch and, when the regulars turned up, it felt like the right choice.

Pugs arrived dressed in amazing outfits. As usual, Barry and Gizmo looked cool and immaculate, rocking bottle-green and red elf outfits with tinkling bells on the end of their hats. Sherlock arrived dressed as Father Christmas, complete with a beard that he seemed to enjoy licking, and Pearl, dressed as a fairy, looked good enough to be put on top of the tree. Doug had a festive sparkly harness on, while Tigs arrived with a collar made from twinkly fairy lights.

Catriona proudly said she'd made it herself. "This Pug Cafe is bringing out my creative side," she joked.

Next, Henry and Percy trotted in dressed as matching snowmen. Bruce was the only dog not dressed up, of course, but that was fine. Hannah didn't need to apologise any more for not "joining in".

After giving everyone a welcome, Anushka spotted her mum nervously sticking her head around the doorway. "Hey, welcome to Pug Cafe," she called to her, grinning and waving her inside.

Anushka struggled to read the expression on her mum's face. Was it surprise? Was she impressed or confused? Her mum glanced around at the props and the pugs, all chasing each other happily around in a whirlwind of waggy tails and tongues, and burst into laughter.

"This place is like Lapland for dogs," Anushka's mum said, shaking her head with amazement. "And you made this all yourself? Anushka! But there are so many people here!"

"We don't just have puguccinos either," Anushka laughed. "Can I get you a coffee?"

Anushka allowed herself a little smile of pride as pugs and their owners came over to say how much they loved the cafe.

Then, Kelly W walked in wearing a Santa hat and carrying Daisy and Lilly. Everyone paused when they realised who it was; even the pugs calmed down, sensing someone special had arrived. Very slowly, one by one, everyone joined in clapping as Daisy trotted around the middle of the community centre, with Lilly protectively behind her as if they were doing a lap of honour. The sisters were proudly dressed as Mother Christmas, with sparkly matching red collars.

Kelly's eyes filled with tears as owners whooped and cheered. "Thank you," she said. "As you can see, Daisy is still doing so well. People even ask me which pug is sick, as they both look so healthy."

Without fanfare, as she didn't want to make a fuss, Ellie stepped forward to let Kelly know how much money had been raised for Daisy.

Kelly waved her hands in front of her face, overcome with emotion. "You lot from Pug Cafe keep me going, you know," she whispered hoarsely. "We don't know how long Daisy has left, but you've created such great memories for her. She's a real fighter. I'm so proud of her." Lilly barked. "And you too, Lilly," Kelly grinned.

Henry and Percy dashed over to lick the pair of pugs before Bertie also stepped in, as if he'd been waiting for his turn.

"Daisy will be around for a while," Hannah reassured her friend.

Anushka felt a frisson of pride as she noticed her mum looking moved. Her mum's face melted with sympathy when Anushka explained Daisy's diagnosis.

"Reminds me of losing Frazzle," her mum said, quietly. "Awful, wasn't it?"

Anushka had never spoken to her mum about Frazzle dying before, and found herself wanting to continue the conversation, but now wasn't the right time. What an emotional Pug Cafe her mum happened to be attending.

At that moment, new faces arrived. Anushka had only "met" them on the Facebook group. Hera and Zeus, a funny pug pair, trotted in behind their owner, Constantinos. He was a tall Cypriot banker with his partner, Scott. They made a lovely couple. Pug Cafe didn't get many men at the events, so everyone made a fuss of them. Hera and Zeus looked and behaved like the spoilt dogs they were. Constantinos even admitted they had home-cooked food every night. Hera's favourite was chicken liver, and Zeus enjoyed steak. Hera seemed to have the upper hand when it came to Zeus too, who followed her everywhere like a henpecked husband.

"Oh yes, they are our babies and rule the roost," Scott laughed. "People actually think Hera and Zeus are husband and wife, you know, as they behave like an old married pair."

As always, Anushka was keeping busy behind the scenes, making sure everything was running smoothly, when she heard a cry from Hannah. "Someone help Bruce, please!"

Anushka dashed over to the sleigh – Bruce had clambered in but was now stuck. Hannah's face had gone bright red, and Anushka didn't know who looked more embarrassed, her or Bruce.

"He's got himself wedged in," Hannah said. "I thought I'd let him have a go for a photo, and now I can't get him out. Oh Bruce, why do things like this always happen to you?"

Bruce glared at everyone with a mixture of irritation and, yes, humiliation, as a crowd of pugs quickly gathered round. Barry and Gizmo made a noise that sounded remarkably like sniggering, so Anushka shooed them away. Hannah gently took hold of Bruce's shoulders while she picked up his hind legs.

"One… two… three…" Anushka counted. "Now… heave!"

But as much as they tried to release Bruce, he held firm. Anushka could feel he was growing hotter by the second as panic set in. She had visions of calling the fire brigade to saw through the sleigh.

But James had an idea. Bruce adored James. He always waited to come up and greet him when nobody else was around. They had a real bromance going on.

"Okay, give Bruce some space," James said, ushering the pugs away. Bertie moved away with a very concerned look on his face. "Right, Bruce," James said, giving him a proper pat on his head. Bruce closed his eyes with relief, as if a superhero with a cape had arrived. "Just calm down, fella, we'll get you out," James added.

James asked Hannah what was the one thing that Bruce found most irresistible.

"Anything on wheels," she laughed. "He turns into Usain Bolt whenever he sees moving parts."

"Okay," said James. "Well, he got himself in, so I reckon he can get himself out."

Everyone hunted around for anything with wheels in the community centre cupboard. Then, as if on cue, Doris appeared at the door in her electronic wheelchair, with her nurse next to her. She looked tired and pale, but beneath her lopsided Santa hat her eyes shone with delight when she spotted the pugs.

"Now, where is my little Daisy and Bertie?" Doris cried, while her chair whirred into the hall.

Bruce's eyes narrowed. He scrabbled like crazy and, pop, jumped like a gazelle out of the sleigh to pursue Doris's wheels. Hannah was mortified as Bruce chased Doris around, but Doris was delighted at such an enthusiastic greeting. She stopped her chair and let him nip at the wheels to his heart's content.

Kelly W had changed Daisy into the cardigan made by Doris and placed the pug on her lap.

"It was my Christmas wish to have a cuddle with my girl," Doris said, pressing her cheek to the pug's. "We both made it to Christmas, didn't we, girl?"

Touched by the scene, Anushka had almost forgotten to look out for her mum. When she glanced over, she noticed she wasn't sitting on her chair any more, so she went to look for her. She checked the kitchen and a side room, but she was nowhere to be seen, so she wandered into the small foyer. There, she could see Doug sitting in his usual Buddha-like pose, with her mum sitting next to him. Cate must have been using the Ladies', and he was waiting outside for her. Anushka opened her mouth to call her mum's name, but stopped mid-step.

Her mum was mid-conversation with Doug, speaking in a candid way she'd never heard before. "Yes, I can't believe all of this," her mum was saying. "All these people brought together. All these pugs. You know my little girl would never say boo to a goose growing up, and now look at her. She's brought people together. Made the most of it being Christmas time. It's really quite something."

A lump formed in Anushka's throat, and she hung back to avoid disturbing them. She didn't want her mum to think she was sneaking up on her, so she slowly stepped backwards, filled with an emotion she couldn't quite grasp.

Thank you, Mum, Anushka thought to herself as she tiptoed off. Even if her mum might not say those words directly to her, somehow it felt good enough to hear her say them at all.

CHAPTER 19

Bertie

I can't decide who my Best Friend Ever is. Sometimes it's Daisy, sometimes Bruce or sometimes Sherlock. Sometimes it's Barry or Gizmo, but, wait, no… today, it's Doug. When you have so many best friends, it's hard to choose.

When I asked Doug to help Anushka's mumma, he did me proud. I saw how he approached her at the right time and asked her to confide in him. All without needing to give so much as a woof. That's Puggy Power for you. Afterwards, Anushka and her mum smiled at each other more than I'd ever seen.

At home that Christmas, I could tell how much happier they were sitting together when they pulled the things that banged – crackers, they called them. They gave belly laughs at the pieces of paper inside. When Anushka's mum left, I thought that next time I wanted to see her smile like that with her sister and dad too. Just like she did in the photos as a child.

Our next Pug Cafe was back with Lovely Biscuit Lady, Nicci. Anushka told me this one was all about love, for what they call Valentine's, but, duh, every day is Valentine's Day for pugs, right? However many times we tell them, humans never understand how much we love them. I have to remind Anushka at least five times a day so she doesn't forget.

I overheard Anushka tell A Man Called James that lots of Pug Cafe members were single. She wanted to do something special for them, as Valentine's Day can be hard if you're alone.

"Ah," I woofed. "With a pug, you're never alone."

They laughed and ruffled my ears. This time they totally understood what I meant.

*

The cafe was filled with balloons and heart shapes, which made me think of Daisy. I missed her and Lilly. The last time I'd seen them was at the Christmas Cafe, when Daisy looked happy even though I'd noticed she'd become slower.

"Knees are creaking in my old age," she'd joked to me. We both knew she was only three. Lilly cocked me an eyebrow with a knowing look, so I chased a balloon with Daisy to take her mind off things. We snuffled goodbye and I said I'd see them soon.

But that was weeks ago now.

At the cafe of love, I celebrated my second birthday too. Everyone sang to me, gave me a special doggie cake and handed me a present. I was allowed to chew the paper off, carefully, Anushka said. Inside was a harness that fitted me perfectly. I raced over to Barry and Gizmo, who'd been watching from the sidelines woofing their approval. Barry looked dapper in his top hat, and Pearl was strutting around in a pink satin bomber jacket.

"I love you all," I woofed at The Best Day Ever.

Well, apart from Daisy not being there. But hopefully I'd see her in The Park soon.

*

As I've said, there are plenty of Best Things Ever about being a pug. But from where I jiggle my tail, I know that however much we help humans, it's not always easy for them. Sometimes, occasionally I'll admit, there are problems that *even us pugs* can't solve.

It was the beginning of March. Anushka had talked on the phone briefly before grabbing her lead. "Bertie, we need to go to The Park now," she called in a wobbly voice. "C'mon, boy."

The skies above were puffy grey, threatening sky water at any moment. I was on my bed having a snoozle, and whined, not wanting to go out.

"Remember, we are dogs from emperors!" I barked, knowing it usually made Anushka laugh. Often, she'd agree and we'd have a snuggle on the sofa with Donkey.

But this time, she clipped on her lead with such a sad face that I decided against making a fuss. *Besides, I may get to see my friends*, I thought. *Yes, this could cheer us both up.* She was right, we should go!

I trotted proudly along, but instead of me taking her for a walk, she pulled me this time as if she was in a real hurry. As I paused for my third pee, she suddenly stopped and pulled out a tissue from her pocket. She pressed it against her own snozzle.

"What's wrong?" I snorted.

Sometimes, humans have their own snuffles like us pugs, but this wasn't what they call a cold. I could smell my human's sadness despite the nip in the air. I nuzzled her shin, and she reached down to sweep me up. In the middle of the street, she buried her face into my ruff. I felt something damp. Tears.

"Oh Bertie," she sobbed. "It's Daisy. She's passed away."

"Daisy?" I woofed. "Is passing by?"

"Yes... Daisy," Anushka whispered.

"Daisy!" I woofed again, licking her tears. "We're going to see Daisy!"

Why was she so upset? I didn't quite understand. I was excited, so I scrabbled to jump down. She set me back down on the pavement, where I did a little happy dance. Seeing her friends would take Anushka's sadness away, whatever was bothering her. This was The Best Day Ever, after all. I pulled on her lead to get there as fast as possible.

Minutes later, we turned the corner to The Park.

"Sherlock! Bruce! Barry! Gizmo! Doug! Oh wow, Lilly!" I hadn't seen Lilly for weeks, so rushed over to do a zoomie around all my favourite faces. "Hello everyone!" I woofed. "Best Day Ever, isn't it!"

Giddy with excitement, I dashed over to Lilly. She was lying down on her haunches, even though it was muddy. Her face was scrunched up with an expression I'd never seen before, so I went to lick her head.

"Where's Daisy?" I barked impatiently, glancing around. Was she hiding in the trees? Playing in a bush? There was one over there that she loved to pee against. "Come out, Daisy!" I woofed. "Lilly needs cheering up." What was wrong with Lilly? "Get up!" I woofed. "Time to play."

Doug appeared by my side. Sherlock pushed his face into mine, so I yelped. He never did this.

"What? What's up?" I barked in his face. "Where's our Daisy Doo?"

"Daisy isn't here," woofed Doug very gently. "Bertie, she's gone to Puggy Place above the sky water."

I looked up – the grey clouds were there but no Daisy. I circled Doug. "What?" I yelped.

"Sit down, Bertie," growled Bruce, loudly, towering over me. "And listen to Doug."

All of the pugs stood in a circle with their heads bowed. Everyone's curly tail lay still. Then, Doug began speaking.

"Daisy passed over the rainbow bridge to Pug Heaven. We won't see her again, Bertie," he woofed softly, looking down at his paws.

"Ever again?" I woofed quietly, fearing the answer.

"No, Bertie. But we can still feel Daisy in our hearts," he said, licking the side of my face.

I glanced over at Lilly, whose big brown eyes were swimming with sadness. Now I was calmer, I could smell how her heart was completely broken. I went over to her, pushed my snout into her ear and held it there.

"Daisy," I whined.

Lilly couldn't reply, as every tip of her fur was yearning for her big sister.

On the other side of The Park, the humans hugged each other. None of Kelly's rolled-up tissues clutched in her hand stopped her eye water. Anushka was holding her other hand. They all looked broken, but I couldn't cheer anyone up. Not right now.

"We loved Daisy," I told Lilly. "And we still love you."

Nobody chased around. Even Bruce wasn't tempted to run after a boy when he flew past on a scooter. Well, Bruce flinched, but he knew better. All our hearts were so heavy, I wondered how anyone's short puggy legs would get them home.

Our humans all said goodbye, one by one, to Lilly's human, who picked her up. Lilly was getting a cuddle all the way home, something I was so pleased about. If I could have, I'd have carried her home myself. I wished I'd brought Donkey so she could have had a cuddle with him too.

All the way home I didn't even stop for a pee. Back in our flat, I went straight to bed for a sad snoozle. My puggy heart ached for Daisy – and for Lilly. All I could see was her sweet face and the scent of heartbreak lingered in my snozz.

When A Man Called James came home, Anushka began to cry. "The cancer had gone to Daisy's brain so there was nothing more they could do," she said through her tears. "They just had to make her comfortable. Lilly hasn't got out of bed for days. All the pugs knew exactly what had happened. Bertie didn't understand at first, but realised when he saw Lilly. Kelly is devastated. I've told her Pug Cafe is there for her when she feels ready for it, but I'm not sure if she'll come again."

*

For the rest of the week, I spent as much of it as possible having a snoozle on my bed. Far from having dreams about Gravy Bones, I dreamt of Daisy giving chase then sitting with me, batting her eyelids looking healthy before she got sick. A few times, I woke with a jump, wondering if it was real or not.

Once, Anushka woke me up gently. "Are you chasing rabbits?" she asked. "Your legs move in your sleep." Actually, I'd been chasing Daisy.

That weekend, A Man Called James drove us to his mamma and papa's house. I hadn't seen Grumpy Grandma for several weeks. When I dashed inside, she raised her head and snorted at me as usual. This time, I wasn't in the mood to play and sat quietly near Anushka.

"Is Bertie okay?" asked A Man Called James's mamma. "He's very quiet."

"Oh, yes, he's not been himself all week," said Anushka. She told them about Daisy while she stroked my ears. Grumpy's ears seemed to perk up. She hobbled up, and came over to me and sat down. Most unusual.

"You okay, kid?" she asked, gruffly.

"Guess so," I woofed.

"Come with me," she said, pawing at the back door. They let us out and stood at the window to watch. For some reason, it amused them to watch us together. I trotted around after Grumpy as she swayed her bad hips, sniffing at the grass. I felt a spot of sky water and recoiled.

"I wanna go back in," I whined.

"Quit moaning, puggy, just for a moment," Grumpy snapped. "Please." I turned my ears down. I could see our humans still gazing at us through the glass. "Do you know where we go after we leave here?" she woofed more softly.

"The Park?" I barked.

She rolled her eyes. "Not this house… This *earth.*" She tapped her paws on the muddy grass. I cocked my head. I had no clue what she was talking about, so thought it best to tilt my head and listen. "'Every dog has his day.' That's what all humans say, right?" she continued, looking around the garden. Sophie seemed to want me to listen to her.

"Yes," I agreed, though I hadn't actually heard this expression before.

"Well, humans chat a lot of guff, but that's actually a true saying," she continued. "Every dog, whatever breed you are, *does* have his day. We're not called A Man's Best Friend for nothing."

"Yes," I woofed, loudly. "That's why I have a Puggy Purpose!"

Grumpy bared her teeth a little. "Yes. That's what you call it. But listen up, mutt, it's *every* dog. And whether we're here for a few weeks or 20 dog years, once we've fulfilled our purpose, as you like to call it, it's time for us to go for our final walk across the rainbow bridge."

"Daisy said she didn't know what her purpose was," I whined sadly. "But she still left us."

"Ah, in that case, she definitely fulfilled it," Grumpy assured me. "We don't always know what it is, but we all have one. Whoever we are. You got that?"

"So where is Daisy now?" I barked sadly. "Doug said she was in the sky."

Sophie looked up again, but not to roll her eyes this time. "Over that rainbow is doggy heaven," she woofed, softly.

My ears perked up. "Do they have Gravy Bones there?" I asked, eyes widening.

Grumpy laughed. "As many Gravy Bones as you like, kiddo." I stared at the sky, ignoring a big splat of water that landed on my noggin. "And our dog body goes into the grass," she continued, tapping her paw. "That's why cats eat it. They'd do anything for our doggie power. But we also leave our paw prints on human hearts, where they remain forever."

I barked loudly at the sky and ran around in a circle until I was giddy. The rain was coming down now, but I didn't mind. I could get soaked for all I cared. I was so happy for

Daisy. And for all of us. One day, we *would* meet again. In my excitement, I rolled in the grass, thinking of all the dogs from the past.

Just then, Anushka opened the door and crouched down, holding her arms open. "Bertie!" she yelled. "It's raining. I thought you'd want to come in."

I looked at Grumpy Grandma, who nodded to show our chat was over. Bolting over to Anushka, I jumped up, leaving muddy paw prints on her cardigan.

"Urgh!" She laughed.

I woofed with delight because I now knew it wasn't just muddy paw prints I'd leave behind on her clothes. One day, her heart would be covered too.

CHAPTER 20

Anushka

Daisy's death shook the Pug Cafe community to its core. Through social media, everyone expressed a longing to pay tribute to Daisy, and they all shared ideas in a private message group.

Jade, the unofficial resident painter, got in touch and offered to do a painting of Daisy and Lilly. Then, Kelly P came up with another idea. She said she was keeping it a secret, but needed every dog's chest measurements and assured everyone that all would be revealed at the next cafe. Anushka's heart was broken for Kelly W, and she hoped that one day she'd feel strong enough to come to another cafe.

Deciding on the next event was a tricky one, as the complaints from disgruntled and disappointed Pug Salon customers continued to mistakenly flood in. Over the past few cafes, Anushka had wracked her brains for new ideas and then, bam, the same thing would be copied a week later by Pug Salon, but not as professionally. James insisted he was still doing his undercover detective work and seemed obsessed with Instagram, but he'd not had any luck uncovering the culprit.

Pug Cafe's reputation was on the line, and Anushka still received emails from people who were concerned about the attacks by the well-meaning vet. Pug Cafe gave her more and more sleepless nights, so she decided there was only one thing for it. She needed to arrange a Pug Cafe event to finally blow all of the competition out of the water. A "make or break" Pug Cafe. Something they could build from again, and firmly establish themselves as the first and the best cafe. But what?

With her energy and motivation levels feeling low, Anushka took Bertie for a walk around Guildford. For a change of scene, she avoided the park and took him near Christ Church, a lovely old stone church with huge stained-glass windows.

As they walked by, they heard the gentle sound of an organ, as suited and booted wedding guests emerged to cheer on the newlyweds. Bertie paused for a quick pee at a lamp-post, but then cocked his head with interest at the proceedings across the road. So Anushka stopped too.

"Okay, Bertie, you old romantic," she laughed. "We'll stand and watch the bride and groom come out."

Soon, a beautiful bride in a long, white off-the-shoulder fitted silk dress emerged, holding the hand of her handsome groom. A cheer erupted as rice was thrown in every direction, making the bride giggle with joy as she waved her bouquet.

Anushka watched as the bridesmaids dived for the bouquet, and it made her smile. She clutched Bertie's lead tighter. "What a happy couple," she whispered to him. "Well, so are James and I. Happy as we are." She tugged at Bertie's lead to leave, but he remained stationary.

He watched in awe as everyone clapped, then lolled out his tongue with pleasure. The guests began nattering as they set off for the reception, now the formalities were over. The best bit for most people!

That evening, Anushka flicked idly through the TV channels, still in a fug about Pug Cafe, when the latest news bulletin flashed up. There, beaming into the camera, was Prince Harry with his new fiancée, American actress Meghan Markle. With arms around each other, they glowed into the TV camera, telling everyone about their wedding plans. There was to be a big royal wedding in May.

"Good for them," Anushka said to James. "They seem made for each other."

She'd seen in magazines how much Meghan Markle loved dogs too. She had a rescue beagle called Guy and a Labrador-shepherd cross called Bogart. Bertie barked at the TV when film footage of Meghan playing with her dogs popped up, with more information on the latest member to join the royal family.

"Wonder if Meghan's dogs will be at the wedding?" Anushka said.

"Can't see the Queen allowing dogs into Westminster Abbey," teased James. "Can you imagine the uproar if one of them peed by a church pew, with billions around the world watching live on TV?"

Pop!

Right then and there, like a light bulb, a brilliant idea for the next Pug Cafe appeared in Anushka's head.

A pug wedding.

When Anushka shared her idea to hold a pug wedding on the same day as the royal wedding, James looked at her with his most doubtful "are you for real?" expression.

"Pugs? Getting married?" he said. He put down the glass of wine he'd poured and covered his face with his hands. James loved pugs as much as Anushka, but he had what he called a more "down-to-earth" view of dogs and their place in the world.

"Why not?" Anushka said excitedly, warming to her idea. "Hear me out. On the exact same day as Harry and

Meghan's wedding, we could hold our own pug wedding. We could have a pug bride and groom, hold a ceremony and then party afterwards. We can have wedding-breakfast dog biscuits and give away wedding-favour goody bags. Come on! Everyone loves a good wedding."

"Do they?" said James, cocking an eyebrow with a smile on his face. "I thought you didn't?"

Anushka couldn't help but laugh. She'd walked right into this one. Arranging a wedding, but for pugs instead of them, was pretty hilarious when she thought about it. She never saw herself as a wedding planner, yet something about it was appealing. But now definitely wasn't the time to bring up the idea of engagement again, so she laughed it off.

"It's not us getting married, silly, it's the pugs," she said.

"But who would be bride and groom?" He laughed. "Bertie? I think he always had a sweet spot for Daisy, but who now? I can't see Sophie agreeing to walk down the aisle with him… well, unless she wanted a toy boy." James began laughing so hard that tears poured down his face.

Anushka pursed her lips, wracking her brains for the perfect pug and wife. Which pugs were suitable contenders? Percy and Lilly had a strong connection, but she couldn't ask Kelly W. She might not be ready for another Pug Cafe yet.

What about Barry and a bride? He certainly loved the attention. Could they even do a gay wedding for Gizmo and

Barry? They were joined at the hip, best pals for life, but she conceded they probably could never love anyone as much as themselves. How about Bruce? Ah, but he didn't like getting dressed up, or many other pugs for that matter. Pearl was full of sass and fiercely independent, and Anushka viewed her as a poster girl for Beyonce's "All the Single Ladies" rather than as a blushing bride.

Then Anushka remembered that pair of dogs, Hera and Zeus, who'd been to the Christmas Pug Cafe, and the comment made by their owners, Constantinos and Scott. "They behave just like an old married couple." The two pugs certainly lapped up attention and loved getting dressed up.

Yes!

Anushka waited until James had finished laughing at his own joke before sharing her idea. "A royal wedding always brings the country together, like no other event," she said. "Perhaps it can do the same for Pug Cafe. So much has gone wrong recently. We just need to put our heart and soul into a special one-off cafe."

James looked serious for a moment as he contemplated the idea. "Actually, Anushka, I think you may be on to something," he replied.

That evening, Anushka sent a message to the owners of Hera and Zeus. They immediately replied, loving the idea.

She also WhatsApped a few Pug Cafe friends, which was how she now thought of them, to tout the idea. The replies were equally enthusiastic. In fact, people said it was the best idea for Pug Cafe they'd ever heard. So, the next day, she set about arranging the wedding of the year.

*

After plumping for the Brighton venue, where a new Astroturf outside provided the perfect place for an outdoor ceremony, Anushka set out the guest list. Already, she had the perfect scenario in her mind. Hera and Zeus would walk down an aisle created from chairs, dressed in pug bride and groom costumes, with the bridal march playing in the background. They'd be followed by bridesmaids, Pearl and Tigs maybe, and pageboy pugs, Henry and Percy, trotting behind them. Sherlock could be best man, and she'd ask Cate if Doug would do the honour of playing the vicar. Last, but of course not least, Bertie could be an usher.

The race to get everything sorted began. Anushka picked heart-shaped flower garlands, designed love-heart-shaped biscuits as wedding favours, made a pug chapel and sketched a seating plan to allow for the bride and groom to waddle down. All she needed now was a pug-sized car for them to drive off in.

During another busy evening of planning, Anushka's phone lit up with a message from her dad. After hearing that her mum had been to an event, he was itching to come to one as well. He even suggested bringing Lakmini. Anushka told him they were welcome any time, but she worried how well this one would go, especially for a "make or break" cafe.

"Lakmini could bring the kids too?" he suggested. Delilah was now 14 and Ruby was eight. They'd have a ball. Anushka felt self-conscious about the idea of her whole family there. But she swallowed down her doubts. The chat she'd had with Dave's son at the care home had echoed in her mind for months afterwards. It was time to create new memories with her own family that outweighed the old ones. Just as Dave had.

"Come!" she said to her dad. "It would be lovely to spend time with you all together."

"Is there anything we can bring?" he asked.

"A pug-sized Cadillac?" She laughed. "Only joking, Dad. It's just a prop I can't get my hands on, however hard I try." She laughed again. "No, seriously, just bring Mum, my sister and those gorgeous girls. It doesn't have to be Christmas for us all to meet up, does it?"

*

Every now and then, Anushka had to remind herself that this wasn't a real wedding. Sometimes, she even wondered whether a real one would be simpler to organise. Sourcing a wedding dress for a pug wasn't the easiest thing to do, and Hera looked less than impressed when Anushka asked Constantinos to try it on her. He sent her a photo of the pug looking less like a blushing bride and more like a humiliated Miss Haversham.

Hera is a law unto herself, he wrote. *But we're hoping we can coax her down the aisle on the big day.*

Anushka dreaded reading about a bigger wedding being organised by Pug Salon in some posh cafe in Kensington or the like, but she put it out of her mind. All she needed to do was make Pug Cafe bigger and better than ever. If this one was a success, she knew she should carry on.

Then, out of the blue, a journalist from *The Times* got in touch, wanting to come along and do a proper review of Pug Cafe. Ordinarily, Anushka would have jumped at the chance – having a review for Pug Cafe in the national press was a PR coup – yet she knew the downsides of this only too well. Already, the pressure was on. If things went badly under the nose of a journalist writing a review, not only would it finish them off, but she'd face public humiliation too.

Once again, the internal Anushka screamed, *Say no. Apologise and make an excuse. You can't handle this – get off the phone before you agree to something crazy.* But her calm voice agreed. "Yes, of course," she found herself saying. "It starts at 11am. I'll make sure your name is on the door. I'll look forward to meeting you." She put the phone down and shoved a clenched fist into her mouth.

"Christ, what's happened?" said James, looking up from the TV.

"I've just placed a high-stakes bet on the next Pug Cafe," she said with a wry smile. "We absolutely have to make sure it goes well now."

CHAPTER 21

Bertie

"Where are these clowns?" whispered Barry, impatiently tapping his too-short nails.

We were waiting between two rows of chairs filled with pugs and humans. Hera and Zeus were due to come down the aisle as pug and groom any second. But there was no sign or smell of them.

Instead, tongues lolled with boredom, some pugs wandered off, and one cocked his leg near a chair, only for his human to shout, "Stop!"

"I dunno," I woofed to Barry. My hackles were rising, and I could see Anushka pacing around, smoothing her hair in the way she does when she's stressed. So I made a mad dash to her side to see if I could help.

"I love yoooou!" I snuffled.

"Not now, Bertie." She shooed me away. "Go on back, just wait a couple more minutes. Hera and Zeus are coming. Well, at least I think they are." Then, she disappeared through a door at the side.

A man with a notebook and pen kept checking his watch and rubbing his chin, frowning. He didn't have a pug, just a camera – and a roving pair of eyes. What did he want? Anushka kept smiling at him all morning, but he never smiled back.

I followed her anyway, as I could feel my heart swell. She was talking to A Man Called James so fast that I could hardly keep up.

"What am I going to do?" she said. "The car's broken. Hera won't wear her bridal gown. Don't even get me started on the cafe's barbecue not working and the Astroturf being out of bounds."

Most human problems are solved with a bath or a cup of that black stuff or tea. But this time, I could sense something was wrong. Badly wrong.

I glanced around. The cafe door had been propped open, and men were going in and out to smoke on their sticks or bring in boxes. Pugs who weren't used to this could make a mad dash. I glanced over at our gang. Everyone was there – even Lilly. For the first time since Daisy died, her human had felt able to come. I lolled out my tongue at her, as I couldn't wait to go for a catch up. But as I glanced back towards the doorway, I saw a familiar curly tail disappearing out of it.

"Sherlock!" Kandeece screamed, leaping from her chair. Suddenly, pugs scattered everywhere while humans grabbed us and the music was switched off. It was chaos. Kandeece ran outside, but quickly stuck her head back in. "Everyone! Sherlock has run off. Right by the busy road," she yelled. "Someone help me catch him!"

Anushka dropped Hera's chewed bridal gown and raced to the door.

A Man Called James followed her. "Don't panic, we'll find him," he assured Kandeece, who burst into tears.

I hopped from paw to paw. What should I do? I desperately wanted to look for my friend, but knew better than to go outside alone. Anushka needed to be on her lead. Amid all the shouting and pug barks, I closed my eyes for a second. *Sherlock*, I thought. *Now where would you go?* I breathed in deeply like he'd taught me. "Take a moment to follow your nose," he'd said.

I could smell biscuits. Fear from Anushka. Worry from A Man Called James. Fumes from the stinky cars. Aftershave from the owners of Hera and Zeus. But what else… a burger? Yes, there was a burger van near this cafe. Then I got a very small note of something else. Cheese! Humans love cheese on their burgers. In that second, I knew exactly where Sherlock was heading.

There must be a burger van selling cheeseburgers nearby.

Excited at my discovery, I bolted out of the door with my nose in the air. I followed the scent, weaving in and out of passers-by who all turned their heads. "Not now! I can't stop!" I barked.

"Is that your pug?" someone yelled at A Man Called James.

"Oh Christ, yes!" he replied. "Thank you. Bertie. Bertie! Come back!"

But there was no time to waste now that my snozzle was on the case. I ran and ran around the corner, then around another one, crossing a cycle lane and over a drain cover. All the while, my snozzle clung onto the trail of the cheddary whiff. Skidding to a stop, I found myself right by Sherlock, who was licking his lips as the man behind a counter in a van laughed at him.

"Go on, then, you can have another one," the man said, chucking a yellow square to land directly on Sherlock's drool-ing tongue. "Now get lost."

"Found you," I woofed.

"Oh blimey, Bertie," Sherlock said. "What you doing here? Not sure he'll give another slice away, I've already cadged two."

"Forget the cheese," I grunted. "Time to get back, fella, there's a wedding we need to get to."

Before I had a chance to turn tail, I felt myself swept up into a sweaty hug.

"There you are!" A Man Called James looked like he'd won the lottery. Which he had, because he was cuddling me. Same feeling, you see!

Kandeece wasn't far behind. She looked happy, cross and relieved all at once as she scooped up Sherlock. Sometimes, watching the number of emotions humans have in one hour, let alone a day, is enough to make me need a snoozle.

"Sherlock smelt cheese. I knew it," she said. "Next time, I'm bringing our own supply."

A Man Called James carried me all the way back in big strides. "We just need to get this ceremony under way now," he said to Kandeece. "Pretty much everything that could go wrong has gone wrong. Poor Anushka. Hera has eaten her costume and won't walk down the aisle, so neither will Zeus. So that's the main wedding ceremony cancelled. And now dogs are running off because staff keep leaving the door open. It's the worst timing with a reporter from *The Times* to see this. God knows what kind of review Pug Cafe will get, if we get one at all."

Kandeece looked as stressed as he did. "Anushka told me her parents were coming for the first time too, but they've been delayed in traffic. She seemed really disappointed they'd walk in to see such chaos."

A Man Called James buried his head in my fur as he took big strides. "This couldn't get any worse," he moaned.

*

As soon as my paws hit the floor, I raced off to find Anushka. She wasn't by the counter. She wasn't by the door. Our humans were chatting, waiting, looking anxious, but she was nowhere to be seen. I dashed into the Ladies' toilet, where she was sitting in a cubicle. I could smell Doug was inside too.

"I did try," Anushka was whispering to him. "Yet somehow nothing worked out. I think it's time to admit defeat. I need to go and apologise to the journalist for wasting his time. I'd better go, and we need to find Bertie too. It's so unlike him to have run off."

"I'm back!" I woofed. I heard the bolt inside slide across.

"Bertie!" She swept me up in her arms. "Oh, I'm so relieved," she said. "Where did you disappear to?"

"We can make it work," I barked. But just when you desperately wanted your human to understand, sometimes they didn't.

"I'm going to have a quick chat with James, and then let everyone know the wedding's off." She sniffed. "I don't blame you for wanting to run away. I'm tempted to do it myself."

Seeing how upset she was, I wondered if she was right. My Puggy Purpose had worked and Anushka had made new friends. Pug Cafe may not have been happening in different cafes any more, but we could still meet in a park, couldn't we? I dashed back down the corridor and bumped into Lilly.

"Bertie, there you are," she woofed. "When is the wedding on?"

"It's not," I replied. "Anushka is cancelling it. This could be the last Pug Cafe too, you know, but we can still be friends, can't we?"

Lilly's perfect sweet face darkened. "Are you *joking*, Bertie?" she woofed.

I lowered my ears. "I know it's sad, but sometimes things don't work out for a reason," I said. "I don't want to see my human worry any more either."

She pushed her face into mine. "Have you any idea how special Pug Cafe is to all of us?" she barked loudly. "You know Daisy did!" Lilly's eyes shone under the lighting as they reflected memories of her sister. "When Daisy lay dying, I sat by her bed for hours. Before she couldn't snuffle any more, she said a few last words: 'Make sure Mamma goes to Pug Cafe.' It was her final wish, Bertie. Pug Cafe can't close. We need it – and now Mamma needs it – more than ever."

I gulped.

"The humans at Pug Cafe make Kelly so happy," she woofed. "You *have* to save it, Bertie. Do whatever it takes. For Daisy."

All of a sudden, Daisy's Puggy Purpose flashed before my eyes. Lilly was right. This was Daisy's legacy. Whatever happened, we had to convince Anushka not to close the cafe. I had no idea how, but I was going to try. If not for me, then for my old friend.

I raced back inside, barking manically to draw all the pugs' attention. "Under the side bench, now!" I woofed.

Barry, Gizmo, Sherlock, Henry, Percy, Pearl, Tigs and Lilly all gathered underneath the bench, with Bruce crouching to listen because he couldn't fit in.

"Okay, listen up," I woofed. "I can say this only once. This wedding *has* to happen. We'll work together. Everyone, dig deep and put on a show for the humans. So they have The Best Day Ever."

I'd only been to one wedding before, and wracked my brains for what humans did. I knew they dressed in white and walked down a corridor with chairs either side. Then, they went outside and cake was involved. I glanced at the cake.

Mmm, cake…

"How?" asked Barry, interrupting my thoughts. He looked put out. A natural entertainer, he'd been sidelined for this big day. I had to find a place for his talents.

"You and Gizmo, you can be the pageboys," I said. "I want you strutting down the front, smiling at all the guests. Bruce, you can be the flower girl… Here." I leapt up and pinched a couple of stems from the table in my mouth and pushed a red-and-yellow flower under Bruce's collar.

He pulled a terrible face. "Geroff," he snapped, trying to nip at it.

I'd forgotten. Our gentle giant hated dressing up more than anything.

"Sorry Bruce, it's for a good cause," I said.

He sat down heavily, scratching at the flowers so a few petals flew off. I didn't have time to argue with him, so just hoped he'd do as I asked.

"I can be a princess bridesmaid," barked Pearl. She knew more about dressing like a human than humans did. Already she looked the part, with her bright pink tutu and gold crown.

"I'll join you, sister," said Lilly. This was unlike her. We loved Lilly, but she usually ran around looking bonkers. It was as though she'd taken on traits of her sensible late sister.

"Good girl," I barked.

"What about me?" Sherlock frowned.

I looked into my blind friend's unseeing eyes and saw how much he loved me, almost as much as cheese. "Best man?" I said. Just stand on the box at the front, howl if you need to, but look regal and stay put."

"You got it!" he panted.

Doug arrived back from the toilet. "I'll get into my position too, Bertie. With our pawsitivity, we can make this work."

"Hang on," woofed Barry. "What about the bride and groom?"

"Leave that to me!" I barked, dashing off to find them.

*

Hera was standing on her tippie-paws on a table, being spoon-fed a puguccino by Constantinos, her human.

"You're a naughty girl, aren't you, hmm?" he chided. "Letting us all down like this. Not wearing the outfit. What are we going to do with you?"

Zeus had his jaw set in a way that told me they'd had a row.

"What's eating Hera?" I whispered to him.

"She's not speaking to me," he whispered back. "The outfit was too itchy for her, so she chewed it off. Says she doesn't want to play. Ah, I dunno, who knows what the lady is thinking."

I stared at him. These two really were like an old married couple.

"What will make her do it?" I asked.

Zeus shrugged. This was hopeless. I paced up and down, aware that the clock on the wall was ticking on and the man with his notepad was tapping his foot. People were talking about looking up train times home. Then, A Man Called James came running in, holding what looked like a shiny car big enough for pugs over his head.

"Anushka, your dad just dropped off this replica Cadillac," he shouted. "Look, it's even big enough for pugs!" Everyone turned and made an oooohing sound at the sight of the flashy shiny pugmobile, as A Man Called James placed the car down at the back of the corridor of chairs. "Thanks for your patience, everyone," he said. "The bride and groom will be along shortly." Everyone cheered and looked at the empty car. It just needed a pug in it now.

I dashed over to Zeus again. I still had no idea how to persuade Hera to get inside the car. What could tempt her? Food? With pugcake crumbs all around her mouth, I guessed she might be full up already.

Miss Pearly came up and pushed her face into mine. "What's the plan, Bertie?" she asked. "Everyone's waiting."

That's when my idea hit me. "Get in the car, Pearl," I whispered. "Don't ask why. Just get in and when I give the nod, get out again pronto."

Pearl looked confused, but did as I asked. She jumped in

and sat upright with her paws on the steering wheel, much to the delight of the crowd. Luckily, A Man Called James sensed something was happening and turned the wedding music back on.

Next, I ran over to Zeus. "Now, you get in the car," I barked.

"What?" he woofed. "But I'm not marrying Pearl." He turned his back on me. Why wouldn't he listen?

I closed my eyes in defeat when I suddenly remembered what Grumpy Grandma had said. "It's all very well being a pug, Bertie, but sometimes you need to be more dog-like."

I got into position, channelling my inner Grumpy. Head down, paws together and… a loud rumble emerged from my throat. "Get. In. The. Car. Now." I growled so fiercely that my own hairs stood up on my back.

Zeus was so startled that he dived head-first from his human's lap next to Pearl in the car.

Whoa, I've never done that before, I thought. *Grumpy Grandma would be so proud.*

Then, before you could say green-eyed pug, Hera glanced up, narrowed her eyes and made a flying leap towards the car, looking as if she wanted to tear Pearl's crown off.

"Pearl, it's your turn," I barked. "Get *out* of the car! Now!"

Just as Pearl jumped out one side, our whining bride landed smack in the seat next to her husband-to-be. My plan had worked a treat. With the bride and groom in the car, there was no time to lose. I knew how contrary Hera was, so desperately needed the car to move immediately. Pearl paced in front of the car with Barry and Gizmo in front of her.

The wedding procession was a go!

Bruce was at the back, with Henry and Percy looking like resident bouncers. Most of Bruce's petals had fallen off, and he cowered as pairs of eyes looked at him as part of the procession.

"Go on Bruce," I whispered, but he resisted joining in. Poor shy Bruce, what could I do to help? Reluctant to use my newfound growl on my friend, a puggy penny dropped. "Look, Bruce," I barked. "Wheels! Go get 'em!"

Bruce's eyes swivelled to the floor, spied the car wheels and his eyes lit up. He took a big dive forward to try and bite them, pushing the car along with his head as he went.

"Lemme at 'em," he barked with delight.

The humans all strained to look at Hera and Zeus being pushed down the aisle in a Cadillac by the biggest, hairiest flower girl they'd probably ever seen.

A Man Called James quickly rushed to stand next to Doug and Sherlock, his face a picture of delight. He spoke a few words as a hush descended over the crowd. "And now I pronounce you pug and wife. You may kiss the bitch."

On cue, Zeus turned and gave Hera a slobbering lick on the chops. I was sure he was licking off cake crumbs, but who cared?

The whole room erupted. Humans stood clapping and cheering, pugs barked and howled. I turned to see Anushka at the back, with tears streaming down her face and her hands over her head, clapping wildly.

Even the man with his notebook and pen was taking pictures with his phone and making whooping noises.

"Do you think we cracked it, dude?" asked Barry from the corner of his mouth.

"I think we did," I barked.

CHAPTER 22

Anushka

Gobsmacked wasn't even the right word for it. One minute, Anushka was walking around the room to quietly tell the guests that Pug Cafe was closing early. The wedding ceremony hadn't quite gone to plan, she'd explained. And if they wished to have tickets reimbursed, they could do so, or if they'd like to stay for their allotted time slots, they were also welcome to do so.

The hottest ticket in town had become the biggest flop. Anushka was resigned to that fact that the fate of Pug Cafe had been sealed. It was time to give up gracefully.

Then, the next minute, Hera and Zeus were sailing down the aisle in the Cadillac, headbutted by Bruce, while Barry and Gizmo tried not to get run over as they strutted their stuff. It had the guests in stitches, their phone cameras at the ready.

Thankfully, James stepped in at the last moment with his prepared ceremony, and Sherlock howled like a choirboy to the music afterwards. Laughter turned to tears at the end, when Hera almost drowned Zeus in drool with her kisses. Anushka wasn't sure if she was just licking wedding-breakfast biscuits off his face, but who cared. It went better than she'd ever dreamt of.

Afterwards, the journalist from *The Times* congratulated Anushka on such a cool and original event. He said the write-up would reflect this, and he couldn't wait to see what Pug Cafe came up with next. "I really have to say I wasn't sure what to expect," he admitted. "But the pugs clearly had a ball. Certainly, it was happier and more fun than any human wedding I've attended."

Anushka admitted she couldn't promise topping this, but would try and come up with something.

While the disco music cranked up for the party to begin, Anushka went to look for her dad. He was nowhere to be seen. It was so kind of him to come and drop off the Cadillac so she longed to thank him. Eventually, she found him standing alone next to the cardboard cut-out of Harry and Meghan outside.

"Dad, why are you hiding out here?" She laughed. "Come inside."

He grinned. "Oh, we just didn't want to bother you while you were busy working. Things looked a little… fraught in there for a while."

"Well yes." She smiled. "We had a few hiccups. But, Dad, you actually helped save the day with that wonderful car. Where on earth did you get it from? Hang on, what do you mean 'we'?"

Dad smiled and waved his hand around the corner, as Mum, Lakmini and Anushka's nieces, Delilah and Ruby, emerged.

"Oh, you all came in the end," Anushka beamed. Her mum came over to give her a hug on one side, while Lakmini joined her on the other.

"We've come to see what my dark horse of a sister has been busy with over the last few months." Lakmini grinned. "When Dad said you'd set up your own business running a cafe for dogs, I thought you might have gone mad."

"Well, I've had my moments." Anushka laughed.

"We watched the pugs marry through the window," said Ruby, stepping forward to hug me. "Grandpa laughed so much, he cried."

"Sorry we're late," said her dad. "Car trouble of our own."

"I never had you down as a wedding planner," her mum teased, nudging her. "This is all very lovely, but is yours next?"

Anushka laughed this off and took her nieces by the hands. They all walked inside together.

After the main marriage ceremony was over, Anushka hoped everyone could relax and mingle, just like guests do at real weddings.

Then, Kelly P came over with a young woman. "Anushka, I want to introduce you to Jade, our secret artist," she said, clutching her hand. "We finally get to meet her. She's come with her mum, Lynette."

Anushka looked at a shy-looking woman with a lovely smile and gave her a hug. She ushered them over to a table so they could sit down and chat.

Lynette's astonishing story about Jade was nothing like Anushka expected. "Jade has learning difficulties and autism," she explained. "And Pug Cafe helped save her."

"Oh my goodness," Anushka gasped. "I think we need a coffee!"

Kelly brought drinks over, and then Lynette explained everything.

"Jade was born with a rare syndrome called fetal valproate syndrome," she said. "It was caused by drugs for epilepsy prescribed for me in pregnancy. I knew something was wrong as soon as Jade was born, and we even had her christened early. But doctors all told me nothing was the matter. She grew up with developmental delays and attended a residential school – the only subject she excelled in was art."

"Jade, you're one of the most talented artists I've ever

met," Anushka told her. "Would you like to meet some of your subjects?"

Being at such a big social occasion was clearly hard work for Jade, as she didn't know where to look. But as soon as Sherlock, Henry, Percy and Bertie trotted over, her face lit up like a Christmas tree.

"It took years of tests and fighting for her," Lynette continued. "Finally, she was diagnosed with her condition at 27. Meanwhile, I helped a campaign to find justice for the women and babies affected by the drug. It was seen as the modern-day thalidomide scandal. I hope one day we can help others affected."

"Good boys," Jade said, giving the pugs a fuss in all the right spots. For the next hour, she was in her element.

Lynette quietly told Anushka how glad she was they'd come along. "Everyone has been so friendly. Jade doesn't have any friends due to her learning disability. But she's been treated like a celebrity this afternoon. She sank into a deep depression after she lost her grandparents in a short space of time, and even stopped doing her drawing until she found Pug Cafe online. She's drawn over 800 pugs so far, and has made so many friends through the Facebook group. I can't thank you enough."

"Oh no," Anushka said, "we should be the ones thanking Jade." Just then, James appeared by Anushka's elbow and asked her to excuse herself. "What's happened?" she asked him, seeing the serious expression on his face.

"I know who it is," he said.

"Who who is? Jade?" Anushka frowned, confused. "Yes, I've just met her."

"No, the person behind Pug Salon," James whispered in a conspiratorial tone.

Anushka excused herself for a moment and took James by the arm to lead him away from everyone else. Right now, she didn't want anything to spoil the atmosphere that people were enjoying. She looked over her shoulder, trying to work out who was missing. Everyone was here.

"Who is it?" she whispered. "How did you find out?"

James took out his phone and showed her an Instagram story for the Pug Cafe account that he'd made the previous week. It was the announcement of a new treat designed by Pug Cafe – he'd even drawn a picture of it.

"I called it a pugalova, made from dairy-free cream and meringue," he explained. "All dog-friendly ingredients, and I said we were having it at the next Pug Cafe. I even mocked up some photos as if you'd experimented making it at home."

"James, you've lost me," she said, impatient to get back to the wedding party.

"Look, Anushka," he said. "I've posted a different pug pudding each day for months, blocking everyone except one

Pug Cafe person each time. Then, guess what Pug Salon brought out as their pièce de résistance at the last cafe? Yes, that's right. At the last event, a few days ago, it was a pugalova."

Anushka's eyes widened. "So whoever saw the pugalova on your Instagram stories runs Pug Salon?" She paused for a moment. "So… who is it?"

"It is…" James said, drawing a deep breath, "Catriona."

Anushka gasped and held her hand to her mouth. Catriona was well-liked. She'd been so wonderful at Nicole's charity event and had helped to raise so much money. People were very fond of her and Allegra.

"I've done more digging and found out that she set up the company with her husband shortly after the first Pug Cafe," James said. "But the last two events were quite disastrous, so they closed early. I don't actually think we have much to worry about any more. Her husband, it turns out, clearly doesn't like dogs as much as she does."

Anushka felt hot with the sense of betrayal. She looked around for Catriona and saw her across the room, chatting amiably to Kandeece. Nobody would have ever guessed it was her. As she thought about what to do next, Kelly P, Pearl's human, took the microphone and cleared her throat.

"Hi everyone, just a quick one," she said. "Sorry to butt in, but I'd like everyone to meet Jade – our resident Pug

Cafe painter. I know many of us are very grateful to her for creating portraits of our much-loved pets."

Everyone clapped, making Jade turn bright red. She looked to Lynette for help, and her mum took her hand for support.

"Jade," continued Kelly, holding a pug toy. "We know you'd like your own pug, so we wanted to present you with a new friend, who I think you're going to call Peggy Sue."

In a fluster, Jade took the toy quickly and put it down next to her. Anushka could tell she wasn't able to deal with the social expectation, and her heart went out to her. So when the clapping died down, Anushka went over to talk to her.

Jade's eyes filled with tears when she told Anushka how happy she was. She held the toy dog as if it was real, looking so chuffed. "Nobody has ever done anything like this for me before," she said.

"Well, you deserve it," Anushka beamed.

"Jade just didn't know what to say, as she wasn't expecting anything," Lynette whispered.

"I understand completely," Anushka smiled. "But sometimes, saying nothing says everything."

Watching everyone chatting and catching up, Anushka decided not to confront Catriona at the party, as she didn't want to ruin such a wonderful ambience. She knew what she'd have to say and how she'd say it, but it needed to be away from Pug Cafe.

*

One of the biggest treats of the wedding day was seeing Kelly W and Lilly smiling again. Everyone wanted to make a fuss of Lilly and check how Kelly was doing. Clearly, the grief was still so raw.

In a quiet moment, Anushka sat down with them for a chat. Kelly said she and Lilly had found themselves locked in a depression. For weeks, Lilly hadn't moved much from her bed. She pined for her sister, roaming around the house looking for her during the day, then wailing helplessly in the garden at night. The Daisy-shaped hole left in their lives was huge.

"My heart's broken, but I couldn't forget that Lilly's was too," Kelly said. She'd kept in touch with everyone from Pug Cafe, confiding how she was feeling. "So I had to pull myself together for her. Everyone at the cafe kept in touch with me online. Sometimes, just offloading to someone after a bad day was what got me through."

Strangely, Lilly appeared to take on characteristics of Daisy after she passed away. She'd grown calmer, more mature, and even started to enjoy having her photo taken.

Kelly took her to a modelling agency, which signed her up. They discovered Lilly had an amazing ability to perch with perfect balance on tiny spaces, so recently she'd been involved in several photo shoots for products such as mini railways.

"Lilly's going to carry on where Daisy left off," said Kelly. "It's given us both a new lease of life."

As they chatted, the cafe grew uncharacteristically quieter. The music was still on, and they heard clattering from the kitchen. But something was missing.

Anushka looked around. "Er… where have all the pugs gone?" she said to James.

She jumped up with alarm, glancing over at the door, which she'd kept shut with a chair in front of it after the earlier escapades. James walked around scratching his head, then disappeared out the back.

Anushka looked around and saw a few of the owners were missing too. She hoped people weren't going home too soon. Not now that Kelly had made the effort to come all this way.

The other Kelly, Pearl's mum, stood up suddenly, with the microphone in her hand.

What was going on?

Kelly W, Lilly's mum, gave Anushka a strange look as if to ask the same thing. Then, suddenly, all the pugs trooped out in a line, one by one, all wearing the same white-and-yellow harnesses covered in daisies.

"As a tribute to your darling girl and our good friend, we'd like to present you with a matching harness, in memory of Daisy," said Kelly P.

Kelly W's eyes immediately filled up with tears. As fast as she wiped them away, more flowed down her cheeks, as Lilly bounded up to her with her new harness on.

"Did you know about this?" Kelly whispered, nudging Anushka.

"Nope," Anushka said, feeling choked with emotion.

Jade then stepped forward with a beautiful painting of Lilly and Daisy together. "I made this for you." She smiled, shyly, before being swept up into a cuddle with both Lilly and Kelly W.

For several seconds, Kelly W struggled to gather herself. Waving her hands in front of her face to hold the tears in, she blew a piece of her fringe out of her face and took a deep breath. "I just want to say 'thank you', not only for this wonderful surprise," she began, "but also for being there for us after we lost our girl. Without Pug Cafe and all our pug friends, I don't think we could have survived. So, from the bottom of my heart, thank you for being our friends."

There was hardly a dry eye in the house as everyone clapped and cheered. Someone raised a puguccino, so everyone grabbed the espresso cups, whether they were empty or not.

"To Daisy!" James shouted.

"To Daisy," everyone cheered. Lilly ran around at Kelly's feet as though she sensed something special was happening.

With all the emotion of the afternoon, Anushka had almost forgotten that this was her family's first Pug Cafe too. She glanced over to see them holding Bertie and watching events with an unmistakable look on their faces – one of pride.

Sometimes, a look someone gives – a smile or a twinkle in an eye – says more than a thousand words. For so long, Anushka had been worrying about the rival cafe. About others taking over the idea and making it bigger and better. About not being able to hire out fancy venues or having capital behind them. But the look on her parents' faces told her that Pug Cafe had something that no fancy venue or rich owner could buy: a place of true friendship. And that was priceless.

Her mum and dad came over to Anushka holding Bertie, who lolled out his tongue with delight.

"And you've been a star too," Anushka said, giving him a good chinny. "Yass, Mummy, that was grrreat," she said in her gruff Bertie voice.

"Someone thinks his mum is very clever and talented for inventing Pug Cafe," Anushka's mum said, holding out Bertie's paw for her to hold. "And someone else's mum couldn't agree with him more."

Her mum and dad stood either side for a cuddle, and Anushka put her head on her dad's shoulder.

"We're so proud of you," he whispered into her ear. "I don't know what to say."

Anushka hushed her dad. "You don't need to say anything else, Dad," she said, smiling.

This was a moment to savour. And with Bertie between them licking their faces, somehow it felt like he'd brought everything together.

Just two years earlier, never in a million years could Anushka have ever imagined attending a party as big as this, let alone organising it herself for strangers. Even more amazingly, she now counted so many of them as her friends. How her life had changed in the time since she'd owned Bertie.

Anushka had always believed in the magic of pugs, ever since she'd fallen in love with them as a teenager. The confident little beings always saw the fun side of life, and somehow Bertie had filled the gap she didn't even know existed. He helped her to seek out the good times, wherever and whenever they were. Not just providing companionship, but miraculously he'd given her confidence to follow a pipe dream.

For a moment, she allowed herself to look around the happy cafe and absorb the joyful faces of owners and pugs alike. With Bertie by her side, she'd taken the journey of Pug Cafe to the hilt. And who knew where it was going to go next?

EPILOGUE

Bertie

I know, I know. It's so hard to choose which day really is The Best Day Ever sometimes, but that's because we pugs have so many of them. If someone offered me Gravy Bones to pick one though, the wedding day could be it.

All day long, my curly tail jiggled like crazy. Except for one moment when things went a bit Pug Tong.

You see, the last of the treats needed eating up before it was time to tidy up. But as we all stuck our snouts in a plateful of wedding cake, Tigs let something slip.

"This cream is almost as good as the pugalova," she woofed.

"Pugawhat…?" I barked. I was certain I'd overheard James talk to Anushka about "pugalovas" because it had got her hackles up. And it was something to do with Pug Salon.

Tigs looked sheepish and sat back on her haunches. Then she stopped eating and looked really sad. She didn't even lick the spot of cream off the end of her snout. "I can't stand secrets," she whined sadly. "It was my owner who made me do it. You have to believe me, Bertie. It wasn't my fault!"

"What are you on about?" woofed Sherlock, his snozzle twitching.

Earlier, he'd told me he could smell other pugs on Tigs we'd never met before… on her lead and collar. Tigs didn't live with any other pugs, so I suggested it must be from a walk.

But Sherlock smelt something else.

Betrayal.

I told Sherlock he wasn't really a detective, even though he was named after one. Tigs was our friend and would never do anything horrible.

"Pug Salon copied your Pug Cafe," explained Tigs, her Disney eyes wide with sadness. "It's my human, Catriona, and her husband who are behind it. They made a pug-alova by copying the recipe from A Man Called James, they said."

Scooby Doo is the stuff of dog legend. My mamma even told me her mamma's mamma had watched it once, way back when it was on TV in the 1980s. Scooby may not have been the coolest dog in history, but with his own van and human posse, us pugs look up to him like nobody else.

When something is revealed to someone, when they're unmasked, that's your "Scooby Doo Moment". Now I recognised this was my first!

But Tigs looked so sad that I couldn't be cross or get excited. I licked her face, sat close next to her and tilted my head to listen.

"My owner loved Pug Cafe so much, she tried to set up her own rival cafe," she woofed, softly. "But they weren't as good as real Pug Cafes, you know. Dogs didn't like them. The humans who came didn't either. Her husband even complained about pugs being pugs. I know deep down he's a… a…" Tig's ears were pressed to her head while she struggled to get her words out.

"A what, Tigs?" I snuffled.

"A cat person," she grunted, and we all huffed in unison at the very thought.

"I'm sorry," I said, licking her face.

"Ah," Sherlock yapped. "I knew something was up!"

Tigs lay down, her head between her paws. She'd been a brave pug for speaking out, but none of us knew what to say. I licked the top of her head as Doug came over. He'd overheard what she'd said.

"None of us can be made responsible for what our humans choose to do with their lives, Tigs," he grunted, wisely. "We can't control their behaviour, however hard we may try."

At that moment, Barry and Gizmo appeared, their nails tapping in time to the beat of a new tune, "Who Let the Dogs Out".

"Why the pug faces?" Barry woofed. "Come and dance, pugs. I wanna see those wiggly behinds on the floor!'"

Tigs perked up. She couldn't resist Barry's invitation. We were just about to join him when Tig's owner rushed over.

"Tigs, darling, are you okay?" Catriona cried. "You look unwell. Oh goodness, it's not the food, is it?" She swept Tigs up in her arms, looking at us suspiciously. "Come on, I think it's time to go. You look like you've eaten far too much cake..."

I could tell she was making an excuse.

Despite herself, Tigs welcomed the unexpected cuddle from her human, and I couldn't say I blamed her. Her owner clearly adored her, and that was the main thing, wasn't it?

We all woofed and howled a loud goodbye to our funny friend. Somehow, I knew everything would be okay. My pug instincts told me that once the dust settled, we would see her again.

*

Later on, back home, Anushka called James over to the Silver Book again.

"Can you believe this?" she tutted. "Catriona has just sent me a long email admitting to absolutely everything. She feels guilty now. She says she'd grown so close to some of Pug Cafe friends she couldn't keep up the pretence any longer after today. Apparently, Pug Salon had been her husband's 'get rich quick' scheme, which she was talked into. She says she understands if she's not welcome any more in the cafes and won't come again if that's what we'd prefer, but she's truly sorry."

"Blimey," said James. "That's a confession and a half. What are you going to do?"

Anushka smiled. "Invite her back, of course." Then she put on her deepest Bertie growling voice. "As long as she brings some pugalova with her next time, Mum!"

That evening, we sat together on the sofa and, for once, the Silver Book was switched off and shut. Happy Days got even better when Anushka pulled out a whole unopened packet of Gravy Bones as a treat for me, stroking my head as I ate them one by one.

"I think you deserve these, Bertie," she said, watching me crunch, as she lifted another from the packet. I'd even had dinner already, so this *was* The Best Evening Ever. "Not only for giving me the confidence to start the cafe, but for somehow making that wedding happen. I don't know how, but I'm sure you were behind it."

"You're welcome," I woofed through a mouthful. "It's my Puggy Purpose, after all."

I chomped at the bones, savouring every last delicious mouthful, jiggling my curly tail to show I was listening as Anushka told me what a brilliant boy I am. Within about 30 seconds, sadly, it was all over, but then I pushed my face forward for a good chinny.

"And who knows where it's going to take us," she continued. "Do you think cafes with other dogs could work? We could do one for Sophie as guest of honour one day, couldn't we?"

I stood to attention and barked. Yes, I'd love to bring Grumpy Grandma along. She taught me to growl, so I can teach her to lighten up and become a bit more puggy.

After so many Best Days Ever, I just *know* there are going to be even better days to come.

Acknowledgments

ANUSHKA:

When I was younger, I spent hours reading books with Frazzle by my side. I especially loved being nosy and reading the acknowledgements at the end, so to be sitting here writing my own (while Bertie is snuggled up snoring next to me!) is surreal and exciting. I am grateful to everyone who helped make this dream come true… 12-year-old me would be SO happy.

Firstly, thank you to Shannon Kyle for bringing this book to life. The stars definitely aligned when I answered that fateful tweet! I'm truly thankful for all your help in telling our story; it's been a pleasure working with you. Thanks to our kind and patient agents, Eve and Ludo at the Eve White Literary Agency, for believing in us and signing your first ever Pug! We are honoured and thank you for all your help. I'd also like to thank our lovely publisher Ajda and her dog-loving super team at Mirror Books for making it all happen.

Without our Pug community this book would not exist! From the bottom of my heart, thank you to every person and every puggy who has ever come to a Guildford Pug Meet or a Pug Cafe event. All my life, I've felt like an outsider looking in, but finally, I feel part of something really special and I treasure the friendships I've made. Special thanks to our friends who contributed to this book, including Constantinos, Hannah, Kelly, Kandeece, Cate, Arti, Nicole and Vicky.

Thank you to Maxine for always, always being there to listen! Thank you to my family, too, for letting me share our story and all your support. Especially to my father, Sunil, thanks for the endless likes and comments on Facebook – you're Pug Cafe's number 1 fan and the hype man every daughter needs!

James, thank you for supporting all my wild ambitions and helping to make my crazy ideas happen. You're so patient and encouraging, and I could not have done any of this without you – you're the lifter, shifter, driver, my business partner and best friend. A loving father to our boys Fox and Bertie and, of course, my soon-to-be husband! Thank you for everything.

To my son Fox, I hope you enjoy reading this book when you're older. Maybe with your own little dog by your side! You're my cookie, the apple of my eye, the sunshine in all our lives and we love you very very much.

Finally, thank you to my co-author Bertie. Things have been tough recently but you're so positive and strong; you're a very special little pug. You have made my life better than I could ever have imagined, you've brought happiness, love and friendship. You changed the course of my life (and took over my bed). I'll always take care of you and promise to get your breakfast out on time! Here's to lots more snuggles and adventures.

BERTIE:

When I was asked to put paw to paper, it was The Best Day Ever. No pug in history has ever written a book before – well not one like this. But after inspiring the world's first dog cafe, who's a better placed pug than me to do it? Nobody, that's right!

I love so many people, I might need another whole book to woof my thanks. But Anushka says I'm only allowed a page, so here goes…

Thank you to Mike and Colin, the pawfect vets who saved my life and my bones. They made me realise the Vee Ee Tee isn't so bad after all and good things can happen. Despite what Marmalade says. Thank you to Nicci, the Lovely Biscuit Lady who let us take over her cafe in Guildford. We'll miss you, your biscuits are The Best! A big thanks to all our pals too, including Bunny, Prince, Frank, Poppy, Nigel, Willow, Elia, Piksy-Rose, Gloria, Bella, Patsy, Stewie, Sumo, Gizmo, Shadow, Larry, Duke, Lady, Lily, Lottie, Henry and Percy and of course Bruce, Sherlock, Doug, Barry, Gizmo, Zeus, Hera, Pearl, and Lilly.

Most of the events in this story are based on real life and now everyone who reads this book will love pugs even more (if that's possible!). Daisy left so many paws on our hearts too, so big woofs until we see your sweet face again. I'm sure you're playing and doing zoomies in the sky. Pug hugs to our friends Pandora, Taz and George who we all miss lots, too.

Thank you to Jade, my birthday buddy, for all your pug hugs and special paintings. They bring everyone in the Pug Cafe group lots of smiles. And thank you to my favourite Grumpy Grandma, Sophie, for teaching me new tricks like drinking from the lake, barking at Kevin and generally being more doggy.

Thank you to my fabulous agents Eve and Ludo for believing in a story only a pug could tell. Anushka was very excited to see my pug face and squishy rolls on your Author page, I could tell it was her Best Day Ever. High paws to our publisher Ajda and her best pal Moby, too.

And finally, last but not least, thank you to Anushka and A Man Called James. For being the best humans a pug could have chosen and for helping me fulfil my Puggy Purpose. Big lick to my human brother Fox, too.

I looooove yoooooooou (almost as much as Gravy Bones. Not quite, but almost…)

Whoops, almost forgot Donkey. Thank you for the snoozles and for never asking to share my dinner! You're the best.

About the Author

Anushka and Bertie the Pug are the founders of Pug Cafe. Together they have created the world's first cafe for dogs and brought thousands of doggies and humans together for a Puguccino!

Famous for organising pop up dog cafes, discos and parties around the UK, they have also built a friendly community of dog owners and lovers.

If you are a dog owner or just love them and you would love to find out where your nearest cafe event is being held or meet some new friends, make sure you join them online now!

www.facebook.com/PugCafeUK
www.instagram.com/pug_cafe
Tik Tok @pugcafe
Twitter @pugcafe

You can also follow Anushka and Bertie's own exciting adventures on their social channels. Give them a follow and say hi!

www.instagram.com/bertieandfamily
Tik Tok @bertiepug
Twitter @Anushka_Tweets

Their events now include cafes for other breeds of dogs too including Dachshunds, Cockapoos, Pomeranians and French Bulldogs. Alongside Mixed Breed events too. To find out more and to get involved visit PugCafe.com